RELIGION IN ILLNESS AND HEALTH

RELIGION
IN ILLNESS AND HEALTH

By

CARROLL A. WISE

PUBLISHERS

HARPER & BROTHERS

New York and London

RELIGION IN ILLNESS AND HEALTH

To my wife,
Addiene G. Wise

ACKNOWLEDGMENTS

THE author gratefully acknowledges the use of material cited from various works. Special acknowledgment is due the following persons and publishers who hold copyrights to some of the material used.

The Williams & Wilkins Company, publishers of *Problems of Ageing*, edited by E. V. Cowdry.

Princeton University Press, publishers of *Symbolism, Its Meaning and Effect*, by Alfred North Whitehead.

Columbia University Press, publishers of *Emotions and Bodily Changes*, by Flanders Dunbar.

The Macmillan Company, publishers of *The Human Personality and the Environment*, by Charles Macfie Campbell, and *Science and the Modern World*, by Alfred North Whitehead.

Charles C. Thomas, publisher of *New Facts on Mental Disorders*, by Neil A. Dayton.

The Blakiston Company, publishers of *Recent Advances in Psychiatry*, by Henry Devine.

Nervous and Mental Disease Publishing Company, publishers of *Medical Psychology*, by W. A. White.

Walter B. Cannon, author of *The Wisdom of the Body*.

The Journal of Comparative Neurology, for material from the work of G. E. Coghill.

The Archives of Neurology and Psychiatry, for material by William A. White.

The Journal of the American Medical Association, for material by E. G. Wakefield and Charles Mayo.

The American Journal of Psychiatry, for material by Flanders Dunbar, *et al.*

The Annals of Internal Medicine, for material by Carl Binger and Flanders Dunbar.

The Psychoanalytic Quarterly, for material by Smiley Blanton.

Mental Hygiene for the use of material previously published by the author in that Journal.

The American Association for the Advancement of Science, for the use of material by the author appearing in *Mental Health.*

TABLE OF CONTENTS

ix

SECTION II. RELIGION IN ILLNESS AND HEALTH

INTRODUCTION

HEALTH has always been a matter of vital concern to intelligent persons. Religion, likewise, has occupied a central place in the life and thought of mankind. In every age and on various levels of civilization religion has been associated, in one way or another, with health and with the experience of illness. Persons gifted with religious insight have believed that religion has something to do with health of body and mind.

There have been many attempts to formulate the relationship between religion, illness, and health in both theory and practice. During the past two decades interest in this problem has developed considerably, not only among clergymen, but among physicians and laymen as well. There has been a growing consciousness that health involves much more than the control of disease, and that illness may be caused by emotional and social factors in the life of the patient. This, together with an increased emphasis on the psychological aspects of religion, has focused attention on the spiritual factors in illness and health. This trend has been increased considerably by the war.

A long experience as Protestant chaplain in the Worcester State Hospital, supplemented by work in the larger community with persons who are representative of the average church member, has given the opportunity to test various theories and approaches to this problem. Contrary to the untutored opinions of many, mental hospital experience leads to a broadening and deepening of one's views on life, health, and religion. Many approaches to the problems involved in the relationships between religion and health have failed to stand the test of such experience because they were too narrow or superficial. Usefulness alone requires an approach that is broad enough to include all pertinent facts from any source and yet specific enough to be applicable to concrete situations. Also, it must grow out of the nature of experience rather than confine experience within a given theory.

Out of this experience the author came to the acceptance of the psychosomatic approach in medicine not only as scientifically sound but also as offering a fruitful approach to problems of religion and health. Indeed, the more the validity of psychosomatic concepts is established, the greater becomes the necessity of understanding the role of religion in the health of the personality. This viewpoint considers the organism as a whole in the light of its total environmental relationships. Thus biological, psychological, and social factors are included in its perspective, and a consideration of the relationship of these factors to each other throws much light on otherwise dark areas of experience. And these factors cannot be thoroughly considered if the religion of the patient is neglected.

From the religious side, there was the constant problem of developing an approach that could be considered as distinctly religious and therefore within the province of the clergyman. There has been in the past decade a tendency for clergymen to step outside their distinctive role and to assume the role of psychiatrist or social worker. This has been unfortunate for all concerned.

It is characteristic of theologically trained persons to view religious experience in the light of some theological, psychological, or social theory of life and religion. Clinical experience, in contrast, centers attention on the living person, and leads to the evaluation of religious ideas and behavior, in whatever degree of pathology or health, in the light of their function in the personality as a whole. With this approach, one cannot escape the symbolic nature of religious expression. Through religious symbols man has formulated his grasp of the meaning and value of life, and has developed a living relationship between various elements within himself and between himself and his world. This relationship finds expression in a way of life and profoundly affects the health of body and mind. While the concept of religion as the total experience of meaning and value is by no means new, the discovery that meaning and value are living realities which in specific ways affect the health of the individual is a distinct contribution of clinical experience. The purpose of this book is to formulate and, to a degree, develop this approach. The author lays no claim to finality or completeness, but rather holds his formulations open to criticism, revision, and further growth.

While the scientific point of view on which this book is grounded has been developing for a number of years, it has become articulate and organized only within the last decade. The appearance, in 1935, of *Emotions and Bodily Changes*, by Dr. Flanders Dunbar, provided a strong impetus, not only to physicians, but also to a small group of clergymen who are studying the problems of religion and health. Recent work in psychosomatic medicine has contributed much that is fundamental to an understanding of the relation of religion to illness and health.

This book is designed not only for clergymen but also for physicians, social workers, psychologists, and others who are interested in the problem. For clergymen it is not intended to be a source of sermonic material nor a book of rules or procedures for producing religious cures of the ill. It is rather meant to be a discussion of basic problems which should serve as a background for the development of the various functions of the clergyman. Again, it is not meant to be a substitute for clinical training for clergymen. There is no substitute for this and it is hoped that the book will convince the reader of the need and value of such training. For other workers and laymen, it is hoped that the book may contribute a basis for answering some of the questions involving religion which are to be found in patients suffering from various kinds of illness, sometimes openly expressed, but always implicit.

There are numerous persons to whom the author owes a debt of gratitude for assistance in the development of this book. Many members of the staff of the Worcester State Hospital, past and present, have been exceedingly helpful. I am especially grateful to the Rev. Dr. Anton T. Boisen, who first opened my eyes to the rich possibilities inherent in the study of mental illness from the point of view of religion, and who provided the opportunity which has been the most valuable educational experience of my life. To the Massachusetts Congregational Conference and Missionary Society, which for many years has generously supported the religious work in the Worcester State Hospital, I am deeply grateful. Those many persons, both on the wards of the hospital and in the larger community, who have permitted me an intimate view of their experience, have been my most enriching teachers. The work involved in the preparation of the manuscript was made possible through a generous grant from the Josiah Macy, Jr., Foundation to the Council for Clinical Training, Inc., to be used for this purpose under the joint auspices of the Council and the Commission on Religion and Health of the Federal Council of the Churches of Christ in America. To each of these organizations, and to the Department of Religion and Health of the Worcester Council of Churches, which also rendered real assistance, the author wishes to express his gratitude. None of these organizations, however, are to be considered responsible for the ideas presented in the book.

The manuscript was read in its entirety by Dr. Andras Angyal, Dr. Walter E. Barton, Dr. William A. Bryan, Dr. Clifton T. Perkins, the Rev. Robert E. Brinkman and the Rev. Seward Hiltner, and in part by Dr. Flanders Dunbar and Miss Marion C. Ely, each of whom made helpful suggestions. My wife, Addiene G. Wise, assisted not only by encouragement and co-operation, but also read the entire manuscript and contributed constructive comments. Mrs. Barbara Wentworth rendered efficient service in preparing the final manuscript.

CARROLL A. WISE

SECTION ONE

ILLNESS AND HEALTH IN THE LIGHT OF MODERN KNOWLEDGE

CHAPTER I

THE MODERN APPROACH TO ILLNESS AND HEALTH

THE PROBLEM

ILLNESS always has been and still remains one of the central problems of human life, while health is something of an elusive ideal. We do know more today about illness than we have ever known before, but this does not prove that we are more healthy. The tremendous medical bill that is paid annually by the American public is just part of the evidence of our failure to master those factors in human existence which lead to illness. Additional evidence is found in the fact that of all the hospital beds in this country more than one-half are occupied by patients suffering from mental and nervous diseases, and that the economic loss resulting from these diseases amounts to more than one billion dollars annually.[1]* To these should be added the losses sustained through crime, delinquency, poverty, family disorganization, and other expressions of individual pathology on the social level. And when such intangible factors as human suffering, misery, and the destruction of human values are considered, much of our complacency in regard to the achievements of modern man should be reduced. For man may send the human voice through the ether to the far corners of the earth, or he may circle the globe in an airplane, or he may conquer certain diseases caused by bacteria. But until he has gone much further in understanding the forces within himself and his society that lead to illness and how these may be turned into the direction of health, he is in danger of

* The numbers appearing in brackets [ ] refer to books and periodicals at the end of each chapter.

losing his own soul. Today man's greatest problem is himself. In the efficacy of the combined efforts of science and religion, each making its unique contribution, lies the hope of mankind for a healthier and more meaningful life.

From the problem as seen in toto, we turn to an individualized expression in the life history of a middle-aged woman.

At the age of fifty-five, Mrs. Smith became very depressed. She found it difficult to sleep, lost interest in her surroundings, and did not enjoy her food. She became increasingly absorbed in the idea that she had sinned. She had no clear ideas as to the nature of her sin, but was sure that punishment would be severe and immediate. Life seemed so worthless to her that she talked about suicide. She was suffering from a mental illness that required psychiatric care.

Certain known facts throw some light on the personality of Mrs. Smith. Her mother died when she was five years of age and she was brought up by an aunt toward whom she never felt very affectionate. Her father had recurring periods of depression, but these were never of extreme severity.

Mrs. Smith finished high school and business school, and worked in offices for several years. She had some difficulty in getting along with her employers, being easily irritated and inclined to become depressed when corrected or when others did not do as she wished. There was a strong tendency to blame herself unduly for her difficulties.

At the age of sixteen she was severely frightened by an older man who attacked her sexually. At twenty-three she fell in love with a man who was disapproved by the family, and her plans for marriage were broken up. Several years later she married a man who was largely her father's choice. She did not love this man, but married him in order to have a home and family. She received no sexual satisfaction in marriage, and always regretted this. Six children were born, all of whom are living and healthy. She experienced the menopause at about the age of fifty, with only minor physical complaints.

Throughout her life, Mrs. Smith was an energetic, active person, who took part in many church and community activities, in addition to carrying the major responsibility in her own home. She had many friends, and was highly respected by all who knew her.

About three years previous to her breakdown, her husband died after an illness of almost a year's duration. Mrs. Smith took care of him during this time. The constant strain made her very tired and restless, and she became slightly depressed. Following his death she blamed herself, without good reason, for not having given him proper care and attention. Periods of depression then came more frequently, and with increasing intensity. She was finally placed in a mental hospital because of the danger of suicide and the need for psychiatric treatment. She responded to treatment and has been free from symptoms of mental illness for the past three years.

HISTORICAL POINTS OF VIEW

Experiences of mental and physical illnesses such as are illustrated in the experience of Mrs. Smith have constituted a problem for mankind throughout the centuries. Before the ancient classic on the problem of suffering, the Book of Job, was written, men sought light on the mysteries of illness. One of the earliest explanations was that of possession by an evil spirit or demon. King Saul, of Old Testament fame, had an experience which apparently was similar to that of Mrs. Smith, and according to the then prevalent interpretation was possessed by an evil spirit.[2] This explanation was very common in the days of Jesus, and the Gospels contain a number of incidents involving persons who were thought to have been possessed. During the Middle Age the belief in demon possession was the theoretical basis on which were devised extremely cruel means of treatment in the belief that intense suffering would drive the demon from the afflicted person. The witchcraft movement in both Europe and America was directed against persons whom today we recognize as mentally ill.

With the rise of the scientific era and the applications of scientific methods to the problem of illness, exciting discoveries took place and a new conception of illness arose. Disease germs and pathological organic processes replaced demons as causative factors in illness. The materialistic and mechanistic point of view came to dominate man's thinking about illness. Man was divided into body and soul, the physician claiming the domain of the body, and the clergy the domain of the soul. All illness was considered to be produced by some physical cause. The task of the clergy in dealing with the ill was considered to be chiefly one of comfort and consolation and, if the efforts of the physician were of no avail, it was his task to perform the last rites. Beyond this the clergyman had no special responsibility unless he belonged to a small minority of unconventional persons who believed in faith healing. All branches of the church spent large sums of money establishing hospitals in which physicians could work and in which sufferers could be treated, as a practical expression of the attitude of the good Samaritan.

On the medical side, another characteristic marked this period. It was an era of specialization. The body was divided among the many medical specialists. This specialization was not only a matter of convenience in treating ill people. It was also a method and point of view for understanding them. It was based on the assumption that the body was to be understood by an analysis of its parts, an assumption which has been properly and relentlessly pursued to the detailed analysis of body cells and obscure chemical processes. Physicians sought to understand each organ as an isolated unit without reference to its relationship to other organs, and to the body as a whole. This era of medicine and the conception of illness on which it was based brought many benefits to mankind, but it also ran into many blind alleys and unsolved problems. "Even now," writes a student in this field, "while medicine copes with exogenous diseases with increasing success, the death rate from degenerative diseases increases steadily, and their etiologic mystery diminishes imperceptibly."[3]

In addition to this, many persons visit specialists of one sort or another every day and are told that they are not really ill, but that it is only imagination. These individuals are victims of illnesses the causes of which can never be discovered by the study of any individual organ, nor by a purely physical approach to their symptoms.

The above sketchy outline of a period of medicine that is passing indicates the basis on which any thought as to the relation of religion and medicine had to proceed. An approach to illness which began by dividing man into body and soul and proceeded by a minute analysis of separate parts of the body could hardly be expected to discover any spiritual factors in illness. In all fairness it should be stated that many physicians, because of their personal insight into their patients, felt the inadequacy of this approach, but were not equipped by training to overcome its limitations. On the other hand, the clergy had become equally blind to possible spiritual factors in illness. There were at least two reasons for this. One was the absorption with the purely intellectual problems arising out of the impact of science on theology, and the endeavor to arrive at an intellectual harmony between the two disciplines. This, of course, tended to obscure the life problems of the individual behind a screen of intellectualized concepts. The other reason was the natural tendency to revere medical science because of its great and beneficial discoveries, and to accept the fundamental premise on which these discoveries were founded. In the area of illness, medical science achieved a prestige which the clergy as a group had neither the basis nor the rashness to dispute. But there were many human sufferers who were not understood by the respectable medical sciences and in whom the respectable clergy found no interest beyond what was with good intentions, but with a certain blindness, termed the "spiritual." Many of these sufferers therefore fell the easy victims of medical quacks or religious charlatans. A perfect scientific, religious, and cultural basis was created for the rise of such movements as Christian Science.

THE MODERN APPROACH TO PROBLEMS OF ILLNESS

Modern medicine is making quite a different approach to the problem of illness, which it is our purpose to elaborate in this section. This approach may be illustrated briefly by reference to the experiences of Mrs. Smith. In evaluating the factors underlying her illness, the physicians arrived at the belief that it was produced by no single cause, but by a number of complicating factors operating on different levels. First, there was probably an hereditary factor. Second, there were possible organic changes owing to the fact that the patient had just passed through the involutional period. Third, there were psychological changes in her personality owing to the same reason. There was also a psychological pattern of adjustment which, under sufficient strain, would produce depression. Fourth, there was a social situation involving particularly her husband's death and her feelings of guilt in regard to his death. All these factors taken together had a definite effect on the total personality of the patient. It is this attempt to approach the experiences of illness from the point of view of the total personality of the patient, rather than some one aspect of the patient's life, that characterizes the modern approach.

The basic difference between the new and the old conception of illness and health lies in their view of the nature of man. The older point of view was materialistic and mechanistic in its approach and divided the body into many parts, attempting to understand each part as a separate unit without considering its relationship to other parts or to the whole. There was no consideration of man-as-a-whole. This is the essence of the new conception. Man, according to the new viewpoint, is to be thought of as an organism which functions as a whole and which possesses an organic unity which makes the whole more than the sum of its parts. The need of knowing all that can be known about any part, the heart, for example, is recognized. But there is an additional insistence that a thorough understanding of the heart, or any other part, requires a study of its relationship to the rest of the organism and its function within the organism as a whole. Furthermore, man needs to be studied as a whole, in order to arrive at a complete understanding of him. "The organism in its totality is as essential to an explanation of its elements as its elements are to an explanation of the organism."[4]

This concept is not new in human thought. Hippocrates, the Father of Medicine, said: "In order to cure the human body it is necessary to have a knowledge of the whole of things."[5] And Paracelsus wrote: "True medicine only arises from the creative knowledge of the last and deepest powers of the whole universe; only he who grasps the innermost nature of man, can cure him in earnest." Other thinkers have expressed similar views. But, as White says, "That concept never became controlling in the efforts of science to explain the living organism. Science was engaged in the discovery of ever more minute structural elements in the make-up of the organism and so always seeking for some explanation back of the facts of observation which it continually hoped would clear up the problem."[6]

However, this new point of view is widespread today. "Throughout all the phases of biological research there is evidence of the same transition from the premise that the whole could be understood by a study of the parts to a new emphasis on the whole. Instead of the concept of aggregates of cells, arranged with increasing intricacy into organs and organ systems as we progress up the scale of evolution to the human being, compounded of psyche and soma, to take his place in the collection of individuals, we have the insistence that the whole is more than the sum of all its parts."[7]

But the person as a whole does not constitute the total problem. The other aspect is the environment in which this person has lived. As we have seen above, the environment of

Mrs. Smith was significant in an understanding of the problems which she faced and the reasons for her illness. This is true of the majority of illnesses. The fundamental problem, then, is twofold: the relation of the organism within itself and the relation of the organism to the environment. This fundamental problem presents "diverse facets to the diverse specialists ranging from philosopher to pure scientist. The physician interested in either the maintenance of health or the cure of illness is working in the dark and by rule of thumb, as a mere technician, unless he has grappled with this problem and reviewed his practice in terms of it. The sociologist, economist or humanitarian, struggling with the problems of the social order, shoots wide of the mark without the perspective afforded by the study of the organism and its environmental relationships."[8]

We have here, for the first time in history, a scientific approach to problems of illness and health which not only offers a basis for a consideration of the relation of religion and health, but which makes such consideration imperative. Whatever else may be said about religion, it is certainly a major factor in the relation of the organism within itself and to its environment. It is the purpose of this book to study into the religious factors in health and illness from the point of view of organism environment relationships. The chapters which immediately follow will elaborate this point of view in order to give a necessary background for later discussions from the religious side.

In seeking an understanding of the problems presented by their patients, physicians who are interested in the whole person and his environmental relationships, rather than in merely the sick stomach or heart, have discovered that mental factors play an unexpectedly large part in the development of many symptoms in both so-called physical and mental illnesses. For a long time it has been generally known that the mind and the body influence each other and that a person could become ill by thinking about being ill. Quacks and charlatans have utilized this general insight to their own advantage, while physicians have sought a physical basis for all illness. It has been only in recent years, however, that some physicians have been developing techniques through which the psychological factors in illness could be demonstrated, and scientific treatment be carried out. Approaching their problem from the physiological point of view, some of these physicians have discovered that physiological processes may not only influence psychological processes, but that they also may be controlled by psychological processes.[9] These psychological processes in turn may be created by relationships between the person and his environment, including, of course, the people in his environment. On the other hand, physicians interested primarily in the psychological approach have discovered that mental factors formed the basis of many of the illnesses with which they were confronted.[10] It is on the basis of these discoveries that a physician can write: "It is not an overstatement to say that fully 50 per cent of the problems of the acute stages of an illness and 75 per cent of the difficulties of convalescence have their primary origin not in the body, but in the mind, of the patient."[11]

REFERENCES

1. POLLOCK, H. M., "Economic Loss Due to Mental Disease in New York State and the United States, 1937," in *Mental Health.* Lancaster, Pa., 1939.
2. I Samuel 16:14-23.
3. STONE, LEO, "Concerning the psychogenesis of somatic disease," *International Journal of Psychoanalysis,* 19:1939, p. 74.
4. RITTER, W. E., *The Unity of the Organism,* quoted by DUNBAR, H. FLANDERS, *Emotions and Bodily Changes,* p. 7. New York, 1935.
5. HEIDEL, W. A., *Hippocratic Medicine.* New York, 1941.
6. WHITE, W. A., *Medical Psychology,* p. 5. New York, 1931.
7. DUNBAR, H. FLANDERS, *Emotions and Bodily Changes,* p. 7. New York, 1935.

8. DUNBAR, H. FLANDERS, *Emotions and Bodily Changes*, p. 3. New York, 1935.

9. See especially CANNON, WALTER B., *The Wisdom of the Body*. New York, 1932.

10. It is primarily to Freud and his fellow workers that credit must be given for the discovery and development of techniques for dealing with the psychological factor in illness, and for the formulation of the results yielded by these techniques. However, it should also be said that other physicians, working with different methods and at times with an anti-Freudian bias, have come to conclusions which are strikingly similar.

11. STRECKER, E., "Mental Hygiene," *Nelson's Loose Leaf Living Medicine*, Vol. 7, Chap. 12.

CHAPTER II

EMOTIONAL FACTORS IN PHYSICAL ILLNESS

For most people, physical illness, or illnesses which manifest themselves through physical symptoms, are common experiences. Mental illness, or illnesses which manifest themselves through mental symptoms, seem to most people, on the other hand, as something strange and remote. Even many persons who are confined in mental hospitals seriously protest that they have no mental illness. This is partially due to the fact that, because of personal and cultural attitudes, physical illness is much more easily recognized by both the victim and his family than is a mental illness. On the personal side, a patient with delusions, for example, is quite likely to accept his delusion as the truth, and therefore to argue that he is not ill. On the cultural side, it is acceptable, and in some quarters quite fashionable, to have a physical illness, whereas it is erroneously considered to be something of a disgrace to have an illness which manifests itself in terms of mental symptoms. As we shall imply throughout this book, illness is illness, and it is neither scientific nor humane to consider persons whose illness takes a mental form in any different light from individuals whose illness takes a physical form. Indeed, some persons whose illness takes a physical form are just as mentally ill as are persons whose illness takes a purely mental form. As one student in this field states: "There is no such thing as a purely psychic illness or a purely physical one, but only a living event taking place in a living organism which is itself alive only by virtue of the fact that in it psychic and somatic are united in a unity."[1]

Because most persons find it easier to think of physical illness than of mental, we shall begin this section by discussing the former type. Incidentally, it should be pointed out that

13

in so far as mental hospital experience is concerned, it makes little difference as to where one begins. In such illness the physical and the mental are inextricably blended, and each must be fully accounted for in any complete understanding of a patient.

Another remark of an introductory nature, bearing on the purpose of this section: our purpose here is not to be technically complete from a medical point of view. Indeed, we shall deliberately and necessarily omit many technical points. Physicians who are interested have their own sources where such material is available; laymen and clergymen would find the material superfluous, if not burdensome.

Our aim in this section is rather to present sufficient material of a general nature to give the nonmedical person an appreciation of this point of view. Nonmedical persons have for many years understood that germs cause certain diseases, though they have not understood the technical aspects of the problem. Likewise, nonmedical persons may and should understand that diseases may be caused by environmental factors other than germs, or by some situation within the life of the person. In other words, a dominating parent or a strong feeling of resentment is just as likely to cause disease as is a germ. Furthermore, and this is of primary importance, such an understanding is essential to any thought in regard to the relationship between religion and health. This material is, therefore, being presented as a necessary background for the succeeding chapters.

Before presenting this material, one caution needs to be sounded, which will be discussed more fully later. The discovery that emotional factors may play a large part in illness opens up new and hitherto unsuspected approaches to the problem of therapy. This problem involves many technical elements which only persons properly trained can understand and utilize. It should be stated explicitly that telling a patient his illness is due to some emotional condition rather than to a disease germ does not put the patient in a position where he can cure himself. Indeed, in some cases it may cause a reaction that is detrimental to the patient. The reasons for this will be discussed later. Here we wish to emphasize that one cannot successfully treat such patients by interpreting their illness in terms of emotional conflict or by trying to talk them out of either their symptoms or their anxiety.

EMOTION IN ORGANIC ILLNESS

The preceding discussion has brought out a point that is of major significance, namely, that emotional factors may play a prominent part in the production of organic illness. Indeed, alert physicians are coming more and more to the conclusion that there is an emotional factor in all illness. The actual significance may vary in each individual case, and it may range from being a more or less complicating factor to being the primary causative factor. But there is no part of the body that cannot be affected by emotion, so intricate and complete are the physiological mechanisms through which emotion is expressed. The discovery of psychological and physiological mechanisms through which emotion influences bodily function places the idea of emotional causation of physical illness entirely within the realm of science as contrasted with mysticism or magic.

That emotional and psychological factors play a large part in the production and treatment of diseases of the heart and of the circulatory system is the belief of many investigators. Concerning angina pectoris, Dr. Harlow Brooks writes: "The spiritual side of the case must not be neglected in this disease in which the emotions play so important a role. The development of a philosophy of life, of the power of adaptation of desire to possibilities, the cultivation of suitable hobbies of a restful character, are of real medical benefit. Habits of restfulness and relaxation are to be cultivated."[2]

That the heart beats faster under emotional tension is a matter of everyday experience. However, there is medical evidence indicating that emotion may not only be a complicating factor in organic heart disease, but that it may also be a causative factor in other kinds of heart and circulatory disorders. Blood pressure, for example, may be influenced by emotion, and high blood pressure is, in many cases, due directly to strong emotional tension lasting over a period of years. One investigator states: "We come to the conclusion that the early fluctuating phase of essential hypertension (high blood pressure) is the manifestation of a psychoneurotic condition based on excessive inhibited hostile impulses. As such, it is a reaction of the individual to the complexities of our present civilization."[3] Other investigators believe that continued emotional tension may produce physiological changes in the circulatory system resulting in an organic lesion, and hence produce chronic high blood pressure.[4] A psychoanalytic investigator has concluded that patients suffering with high blood pressure and also those suffering with angina pectoris show "with striking regularity the presence of intense repressed hatred and resentment and strong guilt-feelings."[5] Another psychoanalyst reports a case where blood pressure dropped to normal and remained there after a therapeutic session in which a repressed childhood experience involving intense guilt and hatred was released.[6]

Turning to another group, the organs of breathing, we find similar medical testimony as to the influence of psychic factors in their functioning. The common experience of holding one's breath in a sudden fright or finding the breath coming in short, quick movements attests in an everyday manner to such influence. That strong emotional states, persisting over a long period of time, may affect the breathing apparatus in a pathological manner is, therefore, not a matter of surprise. Concretely, asthma may be considered as a case in point. Asthma and hay fever are, in many cases, known to have an allergic basis, that is, they are induced by the presence of some foreign object such as pollen or dust. In other cases, however, an emotional factor seems to be the predominant cause. In still other cases, the emotional and allergic factors combine to produce the symptoms. As one research worker writes: "All of these observations would suggest that psychological and allergic factors probably stand in somewhat complementary relationship to each other in the etiology of bronchial asthma, that in some cases asthma attacks may be precipitated by allergic factors alone, in others by emotional factors alone, and that in still other cases, co-operation of allergic and emotional factors may be necessary to produce the attacks."[7] Other writers come to similar conclusions.[8]

Emotional tensions have been found to play a part in laryngitis and the common cold. Concluding a study of 1,667 cases of infections of the upper respiratory tract among Harvard University students, Dr. Arlie V. Bock writes: "Such influences as chilling of the body, weather changes, irritative substances in the atmosphere, and contagion, must be taken into account; but granting these, under ordinary circumstances, the role played by the tension of living must be recognized more generally in our assault on the problem."[9] A psychoanalytic investigator discovered that some persons develop colds in response to certain frustrating experiences which create hostility and anxiety, and that the colds disappeared when the emotional tension caused by the frustration was relieved.[10]

Another set of organs, those whose function is that of digestion and elimination, have been shown by both laboratory and clinical studies to be extremely sensitive to emotional stimulation. The stomach, pancreas, liver, and intestines may respond to such stimulation in two ways: their secretions may be increased or they may be decreased. This is true not only of intense emotional disturbances which are of relatively short duration; it is true also of emotional states in which tensions exist over a long period of time, even though the person may not be aware of it. A common complaint growing out of emotional tensions is so-called "nervous indigestion." As long ago as 1909, Dr. Walter B. Cannon, who has made outstanding contributions to our understanding of the physical effects of emotional tensions, wrote: "The importance of avoiding, as far as possible, the initial states of worry and anxiety, and of not permitting grief and anger and other violent emotions to prevail unduly, is not commonly understood, for the subtle changes wrought by these emotional disturbances are not brought to consciousness, and are clearly known solely through physiological studies. Just as feelings of comfort and peace of mind are fundamental to normal digestion, so discomfort and mental discord may be fundamental to disturbed digestion."[11]

Peptic ulcer is an example of a stomach disorder on which there is much material indicating that the emotional condition of the patient is highly significant for the understanding and treatment of the disease. In a study of 205 cases of peptic ulcer, Dr. Daniel T. Davies and Dr. A. T. M. Wilson found that in 84 per cent of the cases the symptoms began soon after some event affecting the patient's work or finances or the health of his family. Other findings in the same study led them to the conclusion "that peptic ulcer is an example of the influence of the mind in producing structural change, and that successful therapy depends upon attention being given to the whole man—his work and his anxieties, as well as his diet."[12]

Strong emotions, such as fear, anger, and anxiety, may stimulate or inhibit the functioning of the intestines. Accordingly, either diarrhea or constipation results. This may be either acute or chronic, depending on the nature and duration of the emotional tension. Whether a person has one or the other reaction depends on factors not now entirely clear, but physical and psychological characteristics apparently play a part in the determination of the type of reaction. Many authorities could be cited in regard to constipation and diarrhea. In summarizing an article on these illnesses, Drs. E. G. Wakefield and Charles Mayo write: "Persons who have a functional disorder of the colon which may have been excited by social conditions describe symptoms which they believe arise in the colon, but when the colon is examined it is found to be free of physical changes which are indicative of organic disease."[13] They point out that a social crisis of one sort or another is the central cause of such disorders. "The beginning of the first serious disturbance of habit is often occasioned by sickness, accident, unexpected loss of money, property, or a job, or the death of a member of the family, betrayal of confidence of a friend, migration or change of party, church or occupation." They add: "Environmental changes create social crises which are important etiologic factors in functional disorders." They also speak of the presence of fear of disease as a secondary contributing factor. In discussing the treatment of such cases, they say: "It is evident that the cure of these functional disorders is not to be sought merely in certain dietary rearrangements, but in attempts to control scientifically the adverse social conditions. This is not always possible because many patients, from the standpoint of heredity, are incapable of meeting the exigencies of life, and are, therefore, socially pathologic. In order to eliminate these disorders, the defects in education, government, religion, morality, philanthropy and even physical heredity have to be corrected. This ideal may be approached when there is a scientific understanding of the conditions necessary for normal social life. This ideal will never be attained by treating these patients for 'colitis.' "

The findings in a recent study of mucous colitis, a disease in which either of these symptoms may appear, along with others including actual organic lesions, are significant and illustrative. Studying 60 cases of mucous colitis, Drs. White, Cobb, and Jones come to the conclusion that the disorder is "brought about through the action of the parasympathetic nervous system" and that "the commonest source of parasympathetic over-stimulation in patients with mucous colitis is emotional tension."[14] They add that "the three emotions, anxiety, guilt and resentment, are those most commonly associated with tension in patients with mucous colitis."

We have presented material showing that emotional factors play an important role in diseases of the circulatory, respiratory, and digestive systems. Material could be cited showing that emotions also play a part in diseases of practically all other organs of the body. That endocrine glands, the skin, the muscles, the genito-urinary system, and the special sense organs, such as the eye and the ear, may be influenced by the emotional tone of the person is a matter of knowledge. Much light is being thrown on the relation of emotion to diseases involving these organs. Emotional factors also play a causative role in accidents, and are important in the treatment of injuries resulting from accidents, such as fractures. Interested persons may look elsewhere for details.[15] Enough has been given here to illustrate this new development in medicine.

EMOTION IN INFECTIOUS DISEASES

The fact that germs are instrumental in causing certain diseases has been a matter of common knowledge for many years. Typical examples are tuberculosis, in which there is the tubercle bacillus, and typhoid fever, in which there is the typhoid bacillus. But even in such diseases emotional factors are being found today to play a part. "Our attitude toward disease is changing," writes Dr. Carl Binger. "It is no longer satisfactorily explained as a catastrophic invasion of noxious agents, a belief handed down to us, not by bacteriologists alone, but by our more primitive animistic ancestors. We know that it requires more than the tubercle bacillus to make a man tuberculous, more than a specific antigen to produce an asthmatic attack, and more than pneumococci to precipitate an attack of pneumonia. The other ingredient in the disease state was then thought to reside in the 'reaction of the host,' by which was meant in his humoral and immunological defenses. There is now a growing body of evidence which leads to the belief that psychic influences as well, play an important part in the process of falling ill, and that disease, be it infectious, allergic, functional, organic or degenerative, has its developmental history in which the whole personality is involved."[16] A similar point of view is expressed by Dr. C. P. Emerson, who writes: "The bacteriologist . . . no longer teaches that bacillus typhosis . . . is the 'cause' of typhoid fever. It certainly is the only known specific cause, nevertheless the chain of etiology of typhoid fever is made up of other links also, and among them some of which he had named 'immunity,' 'resistance,' 'susceptibility,' etc., and these, he knows, the affective psychical states of the patient can easily modify."[17]

THE INCIDENCE OF EMOTIONAL FACTORS IN PHYSICAL ILLNESS

It is one thing to know that emotional factors play a part in disease; it is another to have some conception of the frequency with which this factor is encountered in physical illnesses. Several studies throw light on this problem. One is a study of 1,200 cases of persons suffering from fractures, diabetes and cardiovascular diseases admitted to a large hospital in a city in the eastern part of this country from 1934-1938.[18] The authors state that "the psychic factor during the period of hospitalization was found to play an important role in the illness of more than 38 per cent of the total admissions. It probably plays such a role in a greater proportion in view of the fact that more than half of the patients admitted had to be excluded from an adequate investigation because the illness at the time of admission was too far advanced (or the situation otherwise unfavorable) to permit the establishing of this fact." In the patients on whom a psychiatric examination was possible at admission, "the psychic factor played an important role in the illness of 79 per cent." In the treatment of these patients, the psychic factor was found to be of significance "in 80 per cent of the patients on whom an adequate examination was made." The authors summarize by saying: "The emotional component is important in the etiology, treatment and prevention of these illnesses, operating by the way of psychosomatic mechanisms." By "psychosomatic mechanisms" they mean processes through which emotion affects organs and organ functioning.

More light on the significance of emotions in illness from the numerical point of view is shed by Dr. Walter B. Cannon.[19] Stating that "in modern life infections have diminished and nervous strains have increased," the author points to a fact that is frequently encountered in medical writings. Statistics show that there is a marked decrease in diseases caused primarily by infections, such as tuberculosis, typhoid fever, and the like, but that there has been a marked increase of diseases of a degenerative nature in which the emotional factor is much more prominent. Cannon states: "Among diseases suggesting strain are those of heart and blood vessels, which have nearly trebled in the last decades. Angina pectoris, emotionally stirred, if not emotionally started, now has in New York and Massachusetts, three times the number of victims as it had in 1900. In New York, exophthalmic goiter, that picture of persistent fright, has consistently increased as a cause of death until it has doubled what it was between 1906 and 1910." And speaking of angina pectoris, Dr. S. R. Roberts writes: "Civilization as we know it in Western Europe and America, the ambition, effort, and community state of mind of these areas, the increasing responsibilities that come with age, and an aging circulation, apparently are the foundations for the increasing prevalence of angina. The inner adjustment to life, the real spiritual control of life, whose outer evidence is a poise and tranquillity of mind, is not very inviting to angina and the anginous life."[20]

A study of a different kind confirms the belief in the great significance of emotional factors in illness today. This is a study made by Dr. Jas. L. Halliday and is based on morbidity statistics in England and Scotland.[21] This author states that illnesses resulting from a combination of emotional and physical factors are often given labels which imply that there is only a physical factor. Such labels, he states, include gastritis, rheumatism, anemia, nervous debility, heart disease, peptic ulcer, chronic bronchitis. In not all, but in many of the patients suffering from illnesses so labeled, the illness is due to emotional as well as physical factors. Studying the morbidity statistics among insured persons in England and Wales, for 1921-1926 and for Scotland for 1930-1936, the author finds that there has been an increase in the average duration of incapacity, that the rise is most marked in illnesses which are given the above labels, and that there is a marked rise in the young age groups. In England and Wales, the incidence of illness increased nearly 50 per cent from 1921 to 1926, while disablement increased nearly 80 per cent. This high level had continued up to the time of this study. In Scotland it was found that between 1930 and 1936 there had been no definite increase in the incidence of "incapacities," but that there was an increase of 11 per cent in their average duration. During the same years, the number of chronic patients (those who were on the sick list continually through the annual period) increased by one-third. The highest rate of increase for all ages was shown by peptic ulcer and gastritis. Next in order of increase were nervous debility, bronchitis, anemia, rheumatism, and cardiac debility. In the 16-34 age groups the highest rise was in nervous debility, bronchitis and anemia and neurasthenia; in the 35-54 age group the highest rise was in peptic ulcer, gastritis, rheumatism, cardiac debility, and diseases of circulation. In no instance was the increase greatest in the old age group. Halliday writes: "The finding that the increase in such illnesses as rheumatism and bronchitis is not in the older age group will surprise only those who have not appreciated the influence of psychic factors as a cause of illness." "It is, therefore, reasonable to conclude," he continues, "that psychosomatic illness is becoming more prevalent and that the maintenance of high rates of morbidity at present existing in the community can only be so understood. No other interpretation covers all the known facts."

CONVALESCENCE AND CHRONIC ILLNESS

This brings us to another important aspect of illness, to which reference has been made already, the problem of convalescence and chronic illness. Strecker has stated that psychic factors are responsible for fully 75 per cent of the problems of convalescence.[22] The material of Halliday, cited above, also pointed to the relation of emotional factors to convalescence and chronic illness. Numerous physicians have expressed the belief that a neglect of the psychic factor in illness, or its mismanagement, is responsible for the fact that many patients seem to recover up to a certain point but never make a complete recovery, even though there is no evidence of organic illness remaining. "There are too many patients today who, already well on their way to an excellent recovery, suddenly and unaccountably develop what we are coming to call the 'chronic invalid reaction' and never quite recover."[18] In the same study it was discovered that of the 1,200 patients studied more than four-fifths were "chronic in the sense that they were not suffering from the first attack of illness in question, or were suffering from an illness which had incapacitated them for more than a year." The authors add: "The psychic factor was of particular importance in the chronic patients in the groups studied, and a large percentage of them were being kept ill unnecessarily by this component of their illness. . . . It is chronic illnesses as well as those illnesses which have the greatest tendency to become chronic in which the psychic component is of the greatest significance to therapy." In another paper Dr. Dunbar cites the case of a patient who had been a chronic invalid for eighteen years in spite of the absence of any demonstrable organic damage.[23] After psychological treatment the patient had remained symptom free for a period of three years, at which time the study was reported. In a later section we shall raise the question as to the effect of religious ministrations on the chronically ill.

THE NATURE OF EMOTION IN PHYSICAL ILLNESS

The preceding material has illustrated the importance of emotional factors in the development of organic illnesses, and in their therapy. We shall now deal briefly with the nature of emotions in such illnesses.

The emotions which underlie various disease symptoms have been identified by investigators as hatred and resentment, guilt and shame, and anxiety. These in turn are the response of the person to situations which produce conflict and frustration. They grow out of experiences that involve psychological suffering and in turn create suffering, such as anxiety. The individual is, therefore, faced with the problem of reducing both the conflict and the psychological suffering which it entails.

In a later chapter we shall deal more fully with the various psychological processes by which a person may reduce conflict and suffering. Here we are concerned with only one, the escape into an organic illness.

Behind the physical symptom there is one psychological fact—the person has attempted to deal with his conflict by the process of repression. Repression is a process through which painful elements of experience are driven from consciousness. It operates not by a deliberate decision of the person, but is rather the result of dynamic tendencies which are part of the whole personality and which function to restore a conscious equilibrium or a conscious relief from tension and pain. Unfortunately, feelings shut out of consciousness still exist in deeper layers of the personality. They are by no means dead, but continue to exert a powerful and unhealthy influence on the organism in proportion to their intensity.

One unhealthy result of repressed feelings, such as anxiety, is the production of physical illness. The fundamental aim of such an illness is that of maintaining as much of a state of conscious equilibrium as possible. The illness is the price the person pays for remaining free of conscious anxiety. But this aim is achieved without the person being aware of it. He, therefore, sees no relation between an anxiety situation which arose some time previous to his illness and the illness itself. He pays the price of illness for relief from anxiety because he was not strong enough to deal with the conflict in a more constructive and healthy way. And there is a certain secondary unconscious gain in his illness which is quite attractive to a weak personality—the gain of attention and sympathy from family or friends, and sometimes the means of dominating the family situation.

The most common emotion found in such illnesses is anxiety. This is frequently related to hate or guilt, either as cause or effect. Whatever the cause of anxiety, it will lead to sickness of one form or another if it cannot be resolved or adequately discharged in activity. The large part played by anxiety has been noted by many investigators. One concludes that "every disease is an anxiety disease. An individual remains sick because he cannot get rid of his anxiety. Hence, to be healthy is to be free of anxiety."[24]

The ways in which emotional factors may predispose to organic illness have been outlined by Dr. Dunbar.[25] First, it has been discovered that many so-called accidents occur because of emotional tensions within the individual. Tension may lead to certain behavior patterns, such as impulsive activity, which result in an injury from the environment. Concrete illustrations of this may be found in Menninger's book, *Man Against Himself*.[26]

Second, emotional tensions may predispose to illness by producing certain changes in physiological functioning. These changes include either inhibiting or overstimulating organs of the body which provide necessary secretions, such as the stomach, or by contracting other organs, such as blood vessels, so that there is not the normal passage for circulation. Emotional tension in some persons stimulates the thyroid gland to overactivity and thus directly produces an illness. On the other hand, it may predispose indirectly as in the case of peptic ulcer, which may result from long-continued overstimulation of the secretory functions of the stomach.

Third, there is an indirect emotional causation for another type of symptom. An example of this is hemorrhoids. These are, in most cases, the result of constipation, which in turn is frequently due to emotional tensions. Dr. Dunbar points out that these symptoms frequently disappear as the constipation is cleared up by psychological treatment.

Fourth, and perhaps of greater significance than these other ways in which emotions predispose to illness, is "the effect on the organism of chronic emotional stress." Emotional stress becomes chronic when it is not fully discharged in appropriate activity and when a person is unable to achieve a full understanding and solution of the conflict. The result of this failure is the perpetuation of physiological changes which normally accompany emotion, and this in turn leads to illness. The relation of chronic stress to organic changes is less understood but just as clear in its effects as are the other ways, and "provides additional background for the contention that to be healthy is to be free of anxiety."

All these ways involve a principle that is encountered also in mental illness. Physical symptoms involve no processes that are not to be found in healthy individuals, but are rather the exaggeration or inhibition of normal processes by emotional tension. This corrects a popular misconception that the "abnormal" individual, physically or mentally, is essentially different from the "normal." The difference is not one of kind, but rather one of degree.

The fact that the emotional tensions which create these illnesses are repressed from consciousness accounts for the inability of sick persons to understand the relation between their feelings and their symptoms or even to recognize that they have such tensions. It is equally true that persons suffering from such illnesses are not aware of anxiety or other such feelings. Their symptoms mask these feelings completely. The person is conscious of being ill, but is not conscious of being anxious. For this reason, it does no good to tell the patient that the cause of the illness is anxiety. Indeed, this may do harm. Cure is effected only through the proper psychological treatment during which the anxieties and their source are gradually uncovered, and through which the conflict is resolved. This requires a skill which only trained workers possess and should not be attempted by others. It is just as dangerous for untrained persons, medical or religious, to tamper with the anxieties of a patient as it would be for them to perform a surgical operation. For the clergyman, the maintenance of a friendly, pastoral relationship, centering attention more on the person than on the illness, with an intelligent use of religious ideas and methods, may give real, indirect help when a direct approach to the illness would result unfavorably.

Not only is there need for a high degree of skill in the treatment of such patients, but even before treatment there is need of skill in the diagnosis. Here, the average physician may not be much more competent than is any clergyman. Adequate diagnosis is a task for the qualified psychiatrist. There is a great difference between the patient who is suffering from a psychoneurosis and the patient who has an organic illness caused by emotional factors. In the first instance, the patient feels the symptoms as being real but has no physiological or organic changes which correspond with these symptoms. An obvious example of this is the remark of a man who was anxious about his wife's illness, and who remarked, "I have a pain where my ovaries would be if I had any ovaries." On the other hand, in organic illness there is always a physical or organic change, and the adequate diagnosis and treatment of this factor is important for the welfare of the patient. In some cases, only physical treatment should be attempted; in others, only psychological treatment, and in still others, both.

Involved in the diagnosis of organic illnesses caused by emotional factors is the exact nature and character of the changes which have taken place. Physicians are thinking in terms of changes in physiological structure which are reversible and changes which are not reversible. It is becoming apparent that a physiological change created by emotional tension may persist over a sufficiently long period of time so that it becomes fixed and permanent. In such conditions, psychological treatment may help the patient in some respects, but will not alter the organic condition. In other patients, the physical changes may not have reached the stage where nature is powerless to restore the organ to its original condition. In such cases, proper psychological treatment may bring about the restoration of physical health. This concept of reversible and irreversible changes is highly significant not only on the physiological level, but also on the psychological and social levels. It will be found useful when we come to discuss the relation of religious factors to health and illness.

Much of the material in this chapter has been organized around disease labels, such as high blood pressure, peptic ulcer, constipation, and others. These labels were the product of an era when attention was focused on specific diseases involving particular organs. On the other hand, throughout this chapter there has been an emphasis on the emotional component in physical illness. That this emotional component may find expression in many forms of illness or through pathological processes in any part of the body has been amply illustrated. To the extent that emotions play a part in any illness, that illness must be considered in the light of the total personality and its environmental relationships. The least important factor in a given illness may be the organ affected. The most important may be a life experience creating emotional tension. The relative significance must be decided in each particular case. But illness can no longer be considered solely as a specific disease of a particular organ. It must be considered as a manifestation of the whole person, and the importance of factors that may seem very remote from the localized disability must be recognized. This fundamental revision carries many implications for treatment and opens the way to a new understanding of illness and health, as well as the relation of religion to the experiences within the total personality which determine the health of the individual.

REFERENCES

1. MOHR, F., quoted by DUNBAR, H. F., *Emotions and Bodily Changes*, p. 116. New York, 1935.
2. BROOKS, HARLOW, "Concerning certain phases of angina pectoris," *International Clinics*, 4: 1928, p. 12.
3. ALEXANDER, FRANZ, "Emotional factors in essential hypertension," *Psychosomatic Medicine*, 1: 1939, p. 178.
4. See WITTKOWER, E., "Studies on the influence of emotions on the functions of the organs," *Journal of Mental Science*, 81: 1935, p. 553.
5. WOLFE, T. P., "Dynamic aspects of cardiovascular symptomatology," *American Journal of Psychiatry*, 91: 1934, pp. 572, 573.
6. HILL, L. B., "Psychoanalytic observations on essential hypertension," *Psychoanalytic Review*, 22: 1935, pp. 60-64.
7. FRENCH, T. M., "Psychogenic factors in asthma," *American Journal of Psychiatry*, 96: 1939, pp. 87-101.
8. WITTKOWER, E., "Studies on the influence of emotions on the functions of the organs," *Journal of Mental Science*, 81: 1935, p. 550.
9. BOCK, ARLIE V., "Acute upper respiratory tract infections," *Annals of Internal Medicine*, 12: 1938, p. 317.
10. SAUL, LEON J., "Psychogenic factors in the etiology of the common cold and related symptoms," *International Journal of Psychoanalysis*, 19: 1938, p. 460.
11. CANNON, WALTER B., "The influence of emotional states on the functions of the alimentary canal," *American Journal of Medical Science*, 137: 1909, pp. 460-487.
12. WILSON, A. T. M., and DAVIES, D. T., "Observations on the life history of chronic peptic ulcer," *Lancet*, 2: 1937, p. 1353.
13. WAKEFIELD, E. G., and MAYO, CHARLES, "Functional and sociological disorders of the colon," *Journal of the American Medical Association*, 111: 1938, p. 1627.
14. WHITE, B. V., COBB, STANLEY, and JONES, C. M., "Mucous Colitis," *Psychosomatic Medicine Monograph No. 1*, p. 95. Washington, D. C., National Research Council.
15. DUNBAR, H. F., *Emotions and Bodily Changes*. New York, 1935.

16. BINGER, CARL, "The psycho-biology of breathing," *Annals of Internal Medicine,* 11: 1937, p. 207.

17. EMERSON, D. P., "The importance of emotions in the etiology and prognosis of disease," *Bulletin of the New York Academy of Medicine,* 5: 1929, pp. 985-1004.

18. DUNBAR, H. F., ET AL., "The psychic component of the disease process (including convalescence) in cardiac, diabetic and fracture patients," Part II, *American Journal of Psychiatry,* 95: 1939, p. 1319.

19. CANNON, WALTER B., "The role of emotions in disease," *Annals of Internal Medicine,* 9: 1936, p. 1453.

20. ROBERTS, S. R., "Nervous and mental influences in angina pectoris," *American Heart Journal,* 7: 1931, pp. 21-35.

21. HALLIDAY, DR. JAMES L., "Rising incidence of psychosomatic illness," *British Medical Journal,* 2: 1938, pp. 11-14.

22. STRECKER, E., "Mental Hygiene," *Nelson's Loose Leaf Living Medicine,* Vol. 7, Chap. 12.

23. DUNBAR, H. F., "Problems of convalescence and chronic illness," *American Journal of Psychiatry,* 92: 1936, p. 1095.

24. DEUTSCH, FELIX, quoted by DUNBAR, H. FLANDERS, *Emotions and Bodily Changes,* p. 90. New York, 1935.

25. DUNBAR, H. FLANDERS, "Problems of convalescence and chronic illness," *American Journal of Psychiatry,* 92: 1936, p. 1098.

26. MENNINGER, KARL, *Man Against Himself.* New York, 1938.

CHAPTER III

EMOTIONAL FACTORS IN MENTAL ILLNESS

EVERYONE is familiar with experiences in which some change in the physical condition of a person results in a change in the whole personality. A case of bona fide indigestion may bring a personality change that turns an otherwise pleasant person into an irritable one. The casual observer is also familiar with the fact that personality changes may arise rather suddenly on the basis of a change in the social situation. The loss of a job or of money may make a person very depressed. Or a minor conflict with a traffic officer may cause some persons to feel that they are being unduly reprimanded. In turn, they may vent their feelings on some innocent party who has difficulty understanding the hostility. External situations that create conflict and frustration lead to various kinds of personality reactions.

The casual observer is familiar with still another kind of minor personality change. This is a change for which there is no obvious physical or social cause. The reason for these changes are to be found in psychological conflicts within the person himself. Popular thinking, which has absorbed a certain amount of psychological jargon, frequently refers to such changes as being due to an "inferiority complex." The average person finds it comparatively easy to understand why physical disability or harsh external circumstances should bring personality changes. But understanding the individual where there is no obvious reason for the change is another matter, and such a person is usually labeled as "queer," or "eccentric," or even "crazy."

Such minor everyday personality disturbances are but miniature counterparts of the more extreme disorders met every day on the wards of a mental hospital. The difference between these minor and major disturbances is not one of kind, but one of degree. The psychological processes involved in these experiences will be discussed later in relation to both minor and major disturbances.

The fact that personality disturbances, whatever their degree of severity, may have their origin on any of the various levels of life serves again to emphasize the point that the personality functions as a whole and that a disturbance on one level may result in corresponding changes in the whole personality. In speaking of severe personality disorders, one authority can write that the physician "is dealing neither with a physical nor a mental disease, but rather with a condition which can only be thoroughly understood and adequately treated when both physical and mental causal relations are taken into account. To discover evidence of somatic changes in a psychosis does not justify the neglect of psychological causal factors. Psychic and physical explanations only represent different aspects of the same reality."[1] This principle has been illustrated in the previous discussion of the case of Mrs. Smith.

The fact that personality disturbances may be caused by improper functioning at any level of life should not be permitted to conceal the additional fact that a personality disorder is primarily a failure of integration that is manifest at the social level. This may be contrasted with failures of integration that are manifest primarily in physical symptoms. A personality disorder always interferes with the relationships between the individual and his environment, particularly with other people in his environment.

In this chapter we shall deal with the problem of mental illness or personality disturbances. We shall attempt to make no hard and fast distinction between major and minor personality disturbances, but shall treat these for what they really are, different degrees of the same kind of experience. Since it is impossible to deal adequately with such a subject within the scope of one chapter, our discussion will necessarily be sketchy. But abundant references will be given for further reading.[2] Our purpose is to give sufficient material to relate this problem to the major purposes of this book, and the reader may look elsewhere for a more detailed discussion.

There is a difficulty inherent in any verbal description of personality disorders. There are subtle aspects of personality which are difficult to capture in words. One becomes acquainted with personalities and the meaning of personality disturbances only through clinical experience under proper guidance and supervision. A book about personality can never be an adequate substitute for clinical experience in the training of clergymen. It is imperative that any professional worker who deals with the intimate problems of personality should be able to recognize what is happening in the persons with whom he is dealing. One of the critical weaknesses of many clergy today is their superficial view of personality and personality disturbances. This may be illustrated by the case of the clergyman who explained the behavior of a young man from his parish as being due to laziness, when in reality he was suffering from a disorder which psychiatrists had already diagnosed as schizophrenia.

MENTAL ILLNESSES RESULTING PRIMARILY FROM ORGANIC CAUSES

Of the new admissions to the mental hospitals in Massachusetts in 1939, approximately 47 per cent were diagnosed as having a form of illness in which organic changes are considered to be a primary cause, 37 per cent were diagnosed as having illnesses considered to be primarily psychological in their nature, and 16 per cent were diagnosed as without psychoses.[3] However, psychological and social factors may play a part in illnesses in which the primary factor is organic, and organic conditions may play a part in disorders which are primarily psychological in origin.

Among the organic changes that create personality disorders are those caused by disease germs, such as syphilis;

those caused by brain injury resulting from accidents; those caused by new growth, such as tumors; by physical exhaustion caused by illness; and by inadequate nutrition, such as vitamin deficiency which is the cause of pellagra. Other organic changes are due to heredity, such as in Huntington's chorea; or to infectious disease other than syphilis, such as epidemic encephalitis. Intoxicants and poisons, such as alcohol, also produce organic changes which result in personality disorders. Mental illnesses in which either hardening of the arteries of the brain or physiological changes which are due to senility are present should be included in this list, as these are usually included in statistical studies as organic reaction types. They are included in the 47 per cent figure cited above. However, psychological and cultural factors are coming to occupy a more prominent place in the consideration of these illnesses. In this chapter they will be discussed as personality disturbances of the aged, and both organic and psychological factors will be taken into account.

Of the remaining illnesses owing primarily to organic changes, those caused by syphilis and alcohol are the most numerous and important, each accounting for approximately 8 per cent of the new admissions. The others account for a comparatively small percentage of the total hospital admissions. In syphilitic and alcoholic groups, important psychological and social factors are involved even though, at the time of acute illness, the major problem may be physical.

The fact that personality disturbances caused by syphilis do occur is itself a symptom of an unintelligent and unhealthy attitude on the part of our culture toward the social situations through which syphilis is spread. Looked at in the large, our culture seems to accept syphilis as a penalty which an individual must pay for the violation of certain cultural standards through activities which the culture itself condemns but also condones. In regard to personality disturbances arising out of syphilis, it should be said that they are absolutely unnecessary and can be prevented. Such personality disturbances almost never arise until years after the original infection, during which there has been ample time for a complete cure to be effected by proper medical treatment. However, the attitude held by the majority of people in our culture operates to prevent adequate treatment. People are afraid their neighbors will discover that they have the disease. One result of this inadequate treatment may be a major personality disturbance.

In general paresis, which is the psychiatric label for the most frequent type of personality disturbance caused by syphilis, there is another interesting psychological problem growing out of the fact that the personality functions as a whole. The particular symptoms shown by a paretic patient depends not on the disease germ, but rather on the general personality make-up of the individual before the illness began. Thus one patient of this type may be depressed, while another may be elated, and still another may show different symptoms. The clinical picture cannot entirely be explained on the basis of the syphilis. As Dr. William A. White expresses it: "Syphilis only disintegrates the machinery with which the individual must work out his salvation and brings his difficulties into the foreground. Syphilis may be the prime reason why an individual has a psychosis but the pathology of paresis will never be able to tell why the paretic has the delusion that he is worth untold millions or that he is God Almighty. It has been pretty well shown that the specific character of his delusions only receives its explanation when his personality make-up is known, when the personality material is understood that is involved in the struggle for expression which the syphilis makes so much more difficult."[4]

It is frequently true that the personality changes caused by syphilis are not recognized as such in their early stages. Early symptoms of general paresis may include difficulty in physical co-ordination, difficulty in concentration, blurring of memory for details, headaches, fatigue, and a deterioration of judgment. Frequently, the early signs of paresis are in the moral sphere. The individual becomes morally irresponsible and does many things which are quite in contradiction to his previous character. It is a good principle to suspect some such organic changes in persons who show these symptoms toward the end of the third decade of life or after. We have known of clergymen spending months trying to re-establish a person whose moral life had suddenly deteriorated, only to discover after a long time that the individual was actually suffering from the early stages of general paresis and was in need of specific medical treatment.

It is unnecessary here to describe in detail the various signs of personality disturbances created by alcohol. It is known that even in moderate doses alcohol decreases the efficiency of motor activity, increases reflex action, lowers physical strength and the point at which fatigue sets in. It also clouds the thinking processes, impairs judgment and the power of concentration, dulls the memory, and creates emotional instability. It is a poison to the cells of the brain.

From the psychological point of view, the problem is: Why do people drink? The belief that the excessive use of alcohol is simply a matter of habit is no longer scientifically tenable. While all the psychological factors are not clear, it is evident that the excessive use of alcohol grows out of deep psychological conflicts. Conflicts and anxiety will produce an organic illness in some persons, but in others it will lead to an excessive use of alcohol as a means of escape from the tension. Personality differences and differences in the nature of the conflict account for the differences in outcome. Thus it can be seen that excessive drinking is primarily a symptom rather than a cause. However, its secondary results are those of organic deterioration. In other words, it can be said that fundamentally the alcoholic is not sick because he drinks, but that he drinks because he is sick, and then becomes doubly sick.

One investigator has summarized the apparent reasons for the excessive use of alcohol as follows: "1. As an escape from situations of life which he cannot face. 2. As evidence of a maladjusted personality, including sexual adjustments. 3. As a development from social drinking to pathological drinking. 4. As a symptom of a major abnormal mental state, such as a depressive or schizophrenic reaction. 5. As an escape from incurable physical pain. 6. As a symptom of a constitutional inferior—a psychopathic personality, i.e., an individual who drinks because he likes alcohol, knows he cannot handle it, but does not care."[5]

It is obvious that the treatment required for any of these forms of personality disturbances resulting from organic changes is primarily medical, although in some cases psychological treatment also may be effective. In regard to disorders created by alcoholism, there is no specific treatment, and each case must be considered on its own merits. The personality disorder created by the alcohol itself may be cleared up by hospital treatment. The effectiveness of psychological treatment is a matter of question. In many patients, it does not seem to be effective, while in other cases it shows good results.

Alcoholism is a form of personality disturbance that has deep roots in the social environment. It is also a grave social problem, which requires a more consistent attitude for its solution. Certainly our tolerance of intemperance and our tendency to interpret the state of intoxication in a humorous way encourages the use of alcohol and means that strong social forces are used for the promotion, rather than the prevention, of alcoholism. The culturally approved commercialization of a need created by a personality illness in a way that results in more harm to the individual is also a serious handicap in the promotion of health. An adequate solution will come in part through providing culturally approved and individually beneficial methods of meeting the personality needs which today are being met by alcohol. At this point, the church has a definite responsibility and opportunity. The problem will not be finally solved by repressive techniques, such as prohibition, but by other measures which lead to a positive satisfaction of the emotional needs of personalities that are created by modern conditions of living.

Mental Illnesses Resulting Primarily from Psychological Causes

In the previous section we stated that approximately 37 per cent of all new admissions to mental hospitals in Massachusetts in 1939 were diagnosed as having an illness primarily functional in nature. In certain other types of personality disorders in which hospitalization is not frequent (psychoneuroses, and antisocial behavior such as crime and delinquency), the primary factor in the disorder is also psychological. This does not mean that there are no organic factors. Rather, it means that, whatever organic findings are present, they are not the major cause of the disorder.

Social and cultural factors play a large part in these disorders, operating by means of psychological processes. These illnesses are the outcome of experiences of intense conflict and frustration of basic urges. As in the organic psychoses, there will be disintegration on the level of social integration, but, in addition, they grow out of the failure of the individual to achieve such integration. In other words, the primary problem in these disorders is the relationship of the individual to the world in which he lives.

In this section we shall deal briefly with the following types of severe personality disorders: the schizophrenias, the manic-depressive psychoses, paranoia, involutional melancholia, disorders of old age, psychoneuroses, and character disorders.

Schizophrenia

Schizophrenia is a type of personality disorder which in the past has been called "dementia praecox." There are several types of schizophrenia. All of them have in common a disintegration between the conscious mental processes and external situations. The emotional responses are inappropriate to the real situation, the patient laughing at a situation in which there is no humor. The person withdraws from external reality, this withdrawal being of various degrees according to the intensity of the disorder. There are peculiarities of behavior and disturbances of the processes of thought.

These illnesses are likely to begin by a gradual absorption of the person in his own problem, accompanied by withdrawal from his external world, extreme shyness, and peculiar mannerisms. Along with this there is usually a great deal of anxiety, and in some cases this anxiety becomes so intense that the individual experiences a panic reaction. In the panic reaction the individual suffers from a very acute fear of practically everything, but the fear of death may be prominent.

The most extreme type of this disease is known as hebephrenia. In this illness there is a deep regression to an early infantile level of behavior, so that the patient behaves in a childish way. Frequently there are hallucinations, and the ideational content is bizarre and incoherent. There are frequently unintelligent mannerisms and inappropriate gestures. Facial grimaces occur with a silly, meaningless laughter. This represents extreme disintegration of personality.

Another form of schizophrenia is known as catatonia. This illness takes the form of either severe disturbance and excitement or stupor. In a given patient, one of these forms may predominate or they may alternate. In the excitement, there is an increase of physical activity, many impulsive actions, frequently of a hostile nature, and delusions of grandeur, usually of a religious nature (that is, the patient thinks he is "Christ," or "the son of God," or some other great religious personage), and ideas that the world is about to come to some catastrophic end. There may also be ideas of death, rebirth, and other bizarre religious ideas.

Another form taken by this disease carries the label "paranoid." In addition to inappropriate emotional responses and hallucinations, such a patient has delusions that he is being persecuted, or has delusions of grandeur, that is, he is some great person. One such patient had the idea that she was the

"Pivotal Point of the Universe" around which everything else revolved.

There is another form of this disease, which is called simple schizophrenia. This is characterized by inappropriate emotional responses to situations in general, lack of interest, and apathy. These patients suffer from unsystematized delusions. The conduct of such persons is irresponsible and mildly antisocial. Many hoboes, prostitutes, and delinquents are suffering from this form of illness, and many such persons never get into a mental hospital.

There are probably some physical factors in many cases of schizophrenia, but these are not clear at the present time. This disease is primarily a result of the failure on the part of the individual to adapt himself to the environmental situation. It is not so much a specific disease as a kind of reaction to a desperate life problem involving the whole personality. In this failure, physical factors may play a part, but the major cause is to be found in conflicts which the individual is unable to solve in a constructive manner. His solution involves withdrawing from his environment and becoming extremely absorbed in his own thinking processes, his thinking becomes dominated by ideas which are the expression of repressed feelings. These are very confusing to him and yet powerful in their control of him. Likewise, his behavior becomes decidedly out of line with usual social behavior and frequently he acts in a childish and even infantile manner.

There is no specific treatment of this disease, either physically or psychologically, but numerous methods are known to produce some good results. At the present time much more is to be achieved in the area of prevention than in the area of cure. Early detection and proper treatment are highly important.

Clergymen should be more familiar with schizophrenic processes than they can become through merely reading about them. Schizophrenic illnesses frequently show religious symptoms in their early stages. These symptoms may take the form of doubts about religious belief, fears about a religious punishment, or an excessive interest in and zeal for religious activities. Many persons suffering from early schizophrenia feel an intense call to preach or to go to the mission field. A sudden and intense interest in religion or a sudden loss of interest in religion needs careful understanding. While it is true that not all persons who have doubts about religion or feel called to religious work are schizophrenic, it is true that many times this illness begins with such ideas.

MANIC-DEPRESSIVE ILLNESSES

Another type of mental illness which is primarily psychological is known as manic-depressive psychosis. Approximately 6 per cent of the new admissions to mental hospitals each year are of this type. It has a higher recovery rate than does schizophrenia.

There are two forms of this illness. In some patients these forms alternate, while in others one or the other predominates. One form is characterized by an elation of mood accompanied by distractibility, flight of ideas, greatly increased activity, and sometimes unacceptable behavior completely out of harmony with the previous character of the patient. Frequently there are delusions of grandeur. The other form is characterized by periods of depression during which the individual is unable to respond normally to his environment. His physical and mental activities are greatly reduced and retarded. He has deep feelings of guilt and ideas of unworthiness and failure.

In considering possible organic factors in the causation of this illness, constitutional and hereditary factors should be mentioned, although at the present time the actual contribution of these is by no means certain and may vary from case to case. Heredity probably plays a more important part in this illness than in most other forms of mental illness. However, psychological factors always combine with a constitutional predisposition to produce the actual illness.

Manic-depressive illnesses are primarily the result of psychological conflicts and frustration to which the individual reacts by a mood change in the direction either of elation or of depression. This type of reaction usually begins with an experience of the loss of a loved object, such as a friend, or money, or position, or a severe frustration arising out of a failure to achieve some cherished goal. Psychological processes of which the patient is unaware and which have arisen in early childhood form the underlying background for this reaction.

The relation of these exaggerated states of elation and depression to minor personality disturbances found in almost every person is significant. Many people become mildly depressed when they experience some loss, while others may find some frustration or reversal to be a stimulant to greater activity. This illness may, therefore, be seen as an exaggeration of a psychological reaction to conflict and frustration that is found in many persons. The reason for this exaggeration may be traced to some constitutional factor or to psychological factors, or to both. In such reactions there are unconscious psychological factors which play a large part.

PARANOIA

A third type of mental illness is known as paranoia. This is to be distinguished from the paranoid form of schizophrenia in that it develops relatively late in life and the only symptoms involved are delusions of persecution and delusions of grandeur. It is a comparatively infrequent disease. Psychoanalysis has worked out a rather complete theory of the genesis of this illness. The classic account of it has been given by Freud in which he interprets the delusions of persecution and grandeur as reactions against homosexual impulses.[6] Later studies have brought out the importance of repressed hostile wishes in the development of these delusions. Whatever may be one's theory of the actual conflict producing these symptoms, this disease is generally accepted as being entirely due to psychological causes. No successful treatment has been developed, principally because of the fact that the paranoiac feels that his difficulty is entirely due to other people and hence it is they and not he who needs the treatment.

Similar to paranoia, but not so extreme, is the paranoid type of personality. These persons are sensitive, shy, and seclusive, and in times of stress have more or less developed ideas of persecution. Such symptoms may be developed to the point where hospitalization is required. However, there are many such individuals in the community who never reach the stage of hospitalization. Frequently they occupy responsible positions and are known as upright citizens. But they are quick to interpret conflict situations in terms of injustice to themselves or as evidence that others are trying to harm them or persecute them.

INVOLUTIONAL MELANCHOLIA

Involutional melancholia is a form of mental illness that has some similarities to the manic-depressive illness, especially the depressed phase. It is not, however, to be confused with the manic-depressive, but should rather be considered as a distinct form. It comprises about 3 per cent of new admissions to mental hospitals, and is more frequent in women than in men.

Involutional melancholia gets its name in part from the fact that it occurs either at the time of or after the climacterium and in part from the fact that the major symptoms are those of melancholia. More specifically, the symptoms are conscious anxiety, agitation, delusions of guilt and unworthiness, frequent delusions of physical illness, strong tendency to self-destruction, preoccupation with the idea of death, hallucinations with ideas of guilt or death, and a loss of interest in the surroundings.

The relation of this illness to physical factors involved in the change of life and in the menopause has been a subject of much study. The endocrine glands were suspected as a major causative agent, and in some cases they seem to play an important role. However, the basic causes of this illness are not to be found in physical difficulties, but in the general personality make-up and life situation in which the patient finds himself.

The involutional period is one of the major transition periods of life. Just as adolescence is the gateway from childhood to maturity, so the involutional period is the gateway from maturity to old age. As such it is fraught with numerous psychological and social hazards, as well as physical, and all these must be taken into account in considering the illness that is peculiar to this age. In other words, the total organism and its environmental relationships are involved in both the involutional period and involutional melancholia.

On the physical level the involutional period is marked by a gradual decrease of physical energy and, in women, a complete cessation of reproductive ability. Psychologically, it marks a turning point from the interests of youth and maturity, characterized by activity, drive and ambition, and physical pleasure, to interests in which these play a diminishing role and in which values such as security, affection, social status are dominant. In our culture, at least, it is a period in which the individual begins to find himself handicapped in competition with the younger group, and where in many relationships, family, social and economic, he is given the impression that he is not wanted, or at least that his value to the group is gradually diminishing. Considering the individual as a whole, this period is one in which the way of life changes, and the individual is faced with the problem of developing a new way of life compatible with changing physical and psychological processes and, of course, within the framework offered by his culture.

The success with which a given person makes the new adjustments required at this age depends on a number of factors. First, the kind of adaptations which he has made up to this time are highly important. The individual who has been able to find real satisfaction in his sexual, social, and vocational life in maturity has a foundation on which he can build for the declining years. On the other hand, the individual who has not found real satisfaction in these important areas, and who, therefore, feels strong frustration, resentment and guilt, will be thereby handicapped in making the new adaptations required. Of special importance at this age are satisfying sexual and family adjustments. One of the secrets of successfully meeting the problems of any of the transitional periods of life is a healthy and satisfying adjustment up to that time. Unsolved personal problems in one period of life are always a handicap in the next period.

Another factor which helps to determine the success or failure of the new adjustments of middle age is the general personality make-up of the individual. This is closely related to the kind of adaptations a person has made up to this time, but deserves separate consideration. In general, the kind of personality most likely to have difficulties is the rigid, inflexible type. This type finds new adjustments difficult. Rigidity of personality is a characteristic of practically all persons who develop involutional melancholia.

Persons who develop this illness show other personality traits with marked regularity. They usually have deep feelings of dissatisfaction, failure and resentment, though these may be well repressed; they are usually very idealistic and have an extremely strong conscience which rides them painfully. They have a strong tendency to enjoy pain and suffering, of which they may not be aware, and sometimes a strong need to make others suffer or at least to be severe in their dealings with others. Their interests are usually narrow, but followed with great zeal and intensity. For this reason they find it difficult to develop new interests at a time when new interests are imperative. Many of them are overly religious, and their religion is of an austere, rigid, and overly idealistic type.

These personality characteristics, along with the inability

to make satisfactory adjustments up to the involutional period, should be thought of as factors predisposing to involutional melancholia. Another set of factors, those which actually precipitate the illness, also should be considered.

Precipitating factors usually take the form of the loss of some person or object to which the person had a strong attachment. Thus the loss of a job, or of a relative or friend, or of one's business, or of some portion of the body through an operation, may create an added tension sufficient to cause a mental illness at the time when the personality is undergoing natural strains and changes. Some persons at middle age are able to stand whatever additional strains life brings to them and to go on to a happy, healthy adjustment. Others, of whom there are a great number, develop only mild neurotic or psychotic manifestations as the result of the emotional conflict, and though they may not be well, neither are they hospitalized. A comparatively small percentage breaks down completely because of the loss of some loved object or source of security, and develops involutional melancholia.[7]

Thus one authority writes: "The involutional psychoses develop not because of too abrupt or too severe a change in the functions of the glands of internal secretion, but because of threatened loss of objects of strong attachment or interference with the feeling of security, in people whose personalities are particularly vulnerable to such crises in adjustment."[8]

While it is not within the province of the clergyman to treat individuals suffering from involutional melancholia, he does have contact with many who are going through deep turmoil at this period. Wise counsel combined with healthy religious attitudes and beliefs may be of great value in meeting both the need for security and the need for love found at this age. Indeed, it may be said that the fundamental problem of this age is a spiritual problem, since it involves the basic meaning of life and the reasons for continuing the struggle. It is characteristic of the persons suffering from involutional melancholia that they have lost their desire to live. Understanding the function of religion in terms of the meaning and value of life rather than in terms of adherence to a creed throws light on its special significance for middle life. Indeed, it might be said that the special task of the personality at the involutional period is that of reorienting itself around values and purposes which are adequate to the needs and strains of later maturity, and which are capable of keeping the personality integrated into a ripe old age. But few clergymen are trained today to deal effectively with this problem.

PERSONALITY DISTURBANCES OF THE AGED

Our declining birth rate, coupled with the increased longevity of life that is due to the efforts of medical science, are making us a nation of elders. A recent study shows that in 1850 the percentage of the total population under five years of age was 15.1, while in 1940 it was 8.3 per cent.[9] The same study shows that in 1850 the percentage of the total population over forty-five years was 12.4, while in 1940 it was 26.5 per cent. In 1850, 2.6 per cent of the population was sixty-five years of age or older, while in 1940, this age group comprised 6.3 per cent of the total population. The same study estimates that, if the present trends continue, in 1980 the percentage of the total population over forty-five will be 40.3, and the percentage sixty-five years and over will be 14.4 per cent. Such a trend raises many social and psychological problems, and not the least of these is the problem of personality disturbances of the aging and aged.

What do mental hospital statistics show about the incidence of personality disorders in this age group? Briefly, they show that, regardless of the emphasis which has been placed on personality disorders in youth, mental illness is primarily a phenomenon of the aging and aged. In Massachusetts, for example, in the year 1939, 4,869 patients were admitted for the first time to mental hospitals. Of this number, 2,450, or more than one-half, were forty-five years of age or over, and

1,104, or almost one-fourth, were sixty-five years of age or over.[10]

A similar trend is seen in the country as a whole. In 1937, 48.6 per cent of all first admissions to mental hospitals were forty-five years of age or over, and 18.9 per cent were sixty-five years of age or over. These figures are significant especially when they are compared with the same age groups in the general population as given above.[11]

Some of the types of illnesses which bring persons of forty-five or over to mental hospitals have been discussed. They are illnesses caused by syphilis and alcohol, involutional melancholia, manic-depressive, and a small percentage from the schizophrenic group. The psychoneurotic group, which will be discussed later, account for a small percentage, though most patients in this group are under forty-five. Two other types which we shall discuss in this section are illnesses with cerebral arteriosclerosis and senile psychoses. These two groups combined make up approximately 20 per cent of the new admissions to mental hospitals each year. But this figure does not tell the whole story. Dayton, in comparing the number of admissions with the number in the population in the age groups actually contributing these admissions, finds that the incidence of these two forms of illness is much higher than had been suspected and much higher than all other forms of mental illness combined. He states: "Either the Senile Psychoses or the Arteriosclerotic Psychoses are showing a higher incidence than all other psychoses combined."[12] These are the primary personality disorders of the aged, the majority of them occurring after sixty years of age.

Recent developments in the understanding of these personality disorders of the aged are revealing the fact that organic changes which take place in age are not their sole cause. It has been definitely shown that aged persons who are not suffering from a mental illness may show, on autopsy, just as much or even more organic damage than aged persons suffering from a mental illness. Thus Malamud writes:

". . . the naive assumption that changes of this type [changes caused by old age] necessarily mean a disruption of the personality has been severely shaken by reports, such as those of Gellerstedt and others, that comparatively advanced changes, particularly of the type found in the senile psychoses can also be demonstrated in brains of normal old people."[13] Rothschild comes to a similar conclusion, and suggests that more important than the actual organic lesion for the understanding of the illness is the person in whom the lesion occurs.[14] This means that the personality organization and the severity of problems arising out of social relationships play a role equal to and in many cases greater than that of actual organic change. Thus in the personality disorders of the aged, in both their mild and their extreme form, we are dealing with the reaction of the person as a whole to problems arising on the physical, psychological, and cultural levels, and the psychological and cultural conflicts and frustrations may be more significant than the physical.

Thus far the physical liabilities of old age have been stressed. But we should be conscious also of the assets of old age, and these are primarily psychological in nature. A valuable contribution at this point is by Miles, which should be read by everyone concerned in a professional way with old persons.[15] Miles points out that, even though physiological maturity is achieved comparatively early, psychological maturity is achieved at a much later date. He shows that, while youth and middle age may make certain achievements and progress dependent on physical energy as well as intellectual capacity, there are other achievements, particularly the development of wisdom, which come only through the ripening processes of age. "The more the behavior product involves experience and considered judgment, the more resistant it is to the psychophysiological age deterioration. The accumulation of information and the exercise of the intellectual functions, together with the controlled organization of emotional attitudes, make possible the development of human wisdom. This is the characteristic prerogative and contribu-

tion of well preserved age." Again he writes: "Where physical stamina and energetic alertness are of relatively greater
account for production than is considered practice, youth
will probably always exceed, but in the exercise of the higher
mental processes, in comprehension, in reasoning and judgment, age alone can develop, through year after year of practice, the qualities of a broad philosophical objectivity."

Our society is predominantly organized for youth and the
values of age are held at a discount. This means that for the
aging person there are two problems: adapting himself to
the changes taking place within, and finding a new status for
himself in a society which makes this increasingly difficult as
the years lengthen. It is extremely difficult for a person successfully to compensate psychologically for loss of physical
vitality if his culture can find no place where his contribution is of value. A society which takes into account individual differences in ability rather than age differences would
be both a happier and a healthier place in which to grow
old.

At this point a comment is in order in regard to the contribution of religion to the aging and aged. This contribution may be made at two points. First, in the declining years
of life, beginning with the involutional period, healthy religious attitudes and beliefs, involving goals and values that
reach out beyond the individual himself, may be of great
value in effecting an integration of personality and giving
a sense of security and worth. In the second place, the church
as such has a definite responsibility in the creation of a
culture in which youth and age can work co-operatively on
common problems, each making its unique contribution.
This must involve the recognition that the religion of youth
and the religion of age will differ, as the needs of youth and
age differ. But more than any other human resource, religion
at its best has an element of universality and timelessness
that is capable of transcending the differences of age and
thereby serving a most valuable function of social integration. It is for the church to solve this problem within its

own doors in order to deal with it effectively within the larger culture.

THE PSYCHONEUROSES

One essential for a healthy personality is a certain flexibility which permits adaptation to new and difficult situations. Another is the capacity to produce concrete results through activity or to achieve consciously accepted goals. Neurotic persons find it difficult to adapt to new or difficult situations. They are also inhibited in the expression of their potentialities and, therefore, fail to produce and to achieve to the extent of their possibilities. They are inhibited because of anxiety, and the strength of the inhibitions is in proportion to the anxiety.[16]

The relation of neuroses to culture has been discussed by various authors.[17] This relationship has two major aspects. One is that the criteria by which a given trait is judged to be neurotic or not depends largely on cultural standards. In some cultures, for example, submissiveness in males is definitely a neurotic trait, as the standard for males in that culture is one of aggression. In other cultures, where the standard for males is one of passivity and submission, such a male would not be considered neurotic. Thus a neurotic trait is one that deviates from the accepted cultural pattern in which an individual lives.

The other aspect is that the culture plays a definite role in the creation of neurotic traits. These traits are the result of the inability to face and resolve the guilt, hostility, and anxiety which are created by conflicts with his culture. The neurotic person deviates from his culture because he has been unable to handle these tensions and remain the kind of person that the culture accepts as its standard.

The following description of the types of neuroses is sketchy and more detailed works should be consulted for further study. The classification of the psychoneuroses has been undergoing changes during recent years and the classification which we shall adopt here will differ from that found in some other works.

One form of psychoneurosis is characterized by obsessions; another by compulsions. These phenomena are closely related. The one is seldom found without the other and the diagnosis is made according to which predominates in the symptomatology. An obsession is a recurring idea that is unacceptable and frightening to the person. An example is a young woman who had the obsession that she would stab someone with a knife and who, therefore, could not endure being near others if there were knives handy. Another is a man who was unable to rid his mind of the idea that God had condemned him.

A compulsion is an uncontrollable urge to some meaningless or harmful activity. A common example is the hand-washing compulsion, in which a person is compelled to wash his hands every time he touches some other person or object. He is compelled to do this because he could not endure the anxiety which he would feel if he did not do it. A compulsion, like an obsession, is a means of allaying an intense anxiety the basis of which is repressed. Pyromania, kleptomania, and some drinking are compulsive.

Compulsive persons sometimes build elaborate but meaningless rituals, such as dressing or undressing in a precise manner. Religious rituals also may become compulsive. When this occurs some unessential aspect of the ritual, such as kneeling, is overemphasized and is allowed to develop into a ritual of itself. In such a situation the person does not kneel in order to pray, but kneels in order to allay anxiety. Such behavior is by no means confined to mental hospitals.

Obsessions and compulsions range in degree from mild cases which attract little notice to severe ones which create intense suffering and greatly handicap their victims. Sometimes they are seen in acute episodes; in other persons, they may become chronic and persist for a long time. In severe cases these illnesses are difficult to distinguish from the schizophrenic reaction. On the other hand, schizophrenic patients often have obsessive or compulsive symptoms.

A second type of psychoneurosis is known as anxiety neurosis. The major symptom of this neurosis is anxiety, the cause of which is not known to the patient. Accompanying this anxiety are physical symptoms, including pains and aches in any part of the body, digestive disturbances, and loss of appetite, increased heart action, extreme fatigue, and perspiration. There is also irritability, inability to sleep, and a lack of interest in general surroundings.

The basic cause of anxiety neuroses is in a repressed conflict. The psychoanalysts view such neuroses as caused almost solely by sexual conflicts, but workers of other schools of thought do not hold to a specific sexual origin for them. It is important to remember that the patient does not know the cause of the anxiety, and the untrained person may err seriously in accepting various explanations which he gives as the real cause. Treating the patient by reassurance or persuasion is usually of no avail and may be harmful.

Another type of psychoneurosis is known as anxiety hysteria. The chief symptom of this is a phobia. The patient has ?n intense fear of a harmless situation or object. Thus he may be afraid to go out on the streets, or he may fear open spaces, or small spaces, or high places, or the dark. The patient may avoid his fears only by avoiding the situation in question.

These phobias serve a protecting function to the patient. While they are disconcerting to him, at the best, they are not so terrifying as would be other ideas or impulses which he has repressed, and which are finding a substitute conscious expression in the symptom. It is impossible to reason such a person out of his fears; the basic conflict must be resolved in order to effect a cure.

A final type of psychoneurosis is known as conversion hysteria. Hysteria has been called the "great imitator" because the hysteria patient may present the symptoms of almost every physical or mental disease. The major symptoms of hysteria are physical symptoms. Disorders of the digestive system and of the respiratory system are common in hysteria. Heart attacks also are a frequent symptom. We would cite the case of a young man who kept his family in a constant state of anxiety by having heart attacks every night. His heart was perfectly sound. The attacks were hysteric in nature.

Other hysteric symptoms involve disorders of sight and hearing. Blurring of the eyes and even blindness can be due to hysteria. Another type of symptom is the inhibition of the ability to receive sensations in some part of the body. Still other symptoms involve some motor activity, and include convulsive movements, paralyses, tremors, and tics. Convulsive attacks often occur in hysteria, and the hysteric may be taken for an epileptic by an unsuspecting person. Sleepwalking, amnesia, and multiple personalities, which are rare, also are symptoms of hysteria.

This list of symptoms could be amplified by much more detail. Enough has been given, however, to indicate the need of adequate diagnosis. Here medical training is essential, and though a layman may be convinced in his own mind that the symptoms of a given person are hysterical in nature, an adequate examination should be made. It should be remembered that the hysteric is always looking for confirmation of his illness and wants it taken seriously. He will be antagonized by efforts to minimize the importance of his symptoms.

In personality, hysterical persons show certain traits in common. They are extremely egocentric, and seek to be the center of their little world. They use their symptoms effectively to get attention and to control their environment. Their view of life in general or of a specific situation is determined solely by their feelings and whether it gives them pleasure or pain. Their need for affection is intense. They are also very suggestible. For this reason their symptoms should not be taken too seriously. An innocent comment on the seriousness of a heart attack may be all that is needed to create one in such a person. Clergymen should carefully evaluate their pastoral techniques in dealing with such people. For example, a prayer that might be beneficial to a person who has a real illness might be quite harmful to an hysteric.

There is no question in regard to the psychological and emotional basis of hysteria. Repressed emotional conflict is always the basis. The repressed feelings are converted into a physical symptom. In this way the conflict is not permitted to reach consciousness. This is known as the mechanism of conversion, and like other unhealthy processes, it serves the purpose of keeping unacceptable feelings, such as anxiety, out of consciousness. A particular organ is selected as the focus of the repressed feeling because it has some special significance or meaning to the person.

It is sometimes difficult to differentiate between a psychoneurosis and a psychosis. Psychiatrists find the line between certain psychoses and neuroses hard to draw in given cases, and the layman is likely to get even more confused. Sometimes it is difficult to distinguish between a possible anxiety neurosis and a depressive psychosis, or an obsessional neurosis and schizophrenia. This is because of the fact that these illnesses do not represent disease entities, but are rather reactions to a life situation. As such, they may overlap and blend into each other, so that more than one kind of symptom is found in a given person. Psychoanalysts believe that the type of reaction is determined by the level of personality development on which the primary conflict occurs. Thus they place the schizophrenic reactions on the level from birth to approximately two years and the neurotic reaction from approximately one year up to six or seven years. However, it should be emphasized that it is not the age of the child in terms of years that is most important. It is the kind of experience that the child is having at these ages. Thus conflicts in regard to weaning, sphincter control, the arrival of a new infant in the home, the necessity of accepting the social standards of the home, conflict over infantile masturbation, occur at different age levels. These in turn may result in different reactions depending on the ability of the child to cope with them and the kind of assistance he receives from his parents and others in his environment. The development of personality cannot be charted in a fixed form, but varies in different persons. Likewise, a person may develop a clear-cut neurosis, or a clear-cut psychosis, or an illness that has symptoms of each.

In general it can be said that a psychosis involves a change in the total personality and in the relations of the person to reality. A psychoneurosis, on the other hand, involves only part of the personality, and the person is able to continue many of his relationships with his environment comparatively undisturbed. Many persons suffering from neuroses hold responsible positions in all phases of social life, including the church, state, business, medicine, and education. This has both beneficial and adverse results. The adverse results depend largely on the extent to which the neurotic person has the opportunity to influence or control the lives of others, particularly of children.

Another important difference between the neurotic and the psychotic person is that the neurotic realizes that something is wrong with him and can describe his symptoms in accurate detail, while the psychotic does not know that he is sick. The neurotic person knows that some of his ideas and actions are not in conformity with reality; the psychotic person accepts his own ideas and behavior as reality and complains that the world does not agree with him.

The reason for this difference in insight is the fact that the conscious processes of thought and understanding are not disintegrated in the neurotic person as they are in the psychotic person. The neurotic conflict is not so deep, and his regression to infantile forms of response is not so great. In other words, his ego is more preserved.

The fact that the neurotic person knows that he is different is a source of severe suffering to him. This suffering, however, should not be confused with the basic anxiety which creates the neurosis and which the person has repressed. The feeling of inferiority in many neurotic persons is the result of their neuroses, not the cause. Such persons are usually skillful in gaining certain secondary ends, such as the sympathy of others because of their conscious suffering, and may make heavy and impossible demands on family and friends. They also get a certain masochistic pleasure out of the suffering, or as is popularly remarked, they "enjoy ill-health." These two factors may operate to perpetuate the illness and hinder cure.

There are, of course, other differences between neuroses and psychoses, but to discuss these would lead us into more technical material than is desirable here. However, there are sources in which this material may be found.[18]

Everyone who works directly with other persons should have at least a general knowledge of the meaning of neurotic behavior in its various forms. If there were no other reason for such knowledge, the fact that such behavior is so common is sufficient. Beyond this, however, there is the fact that neurotic persons may be seriously hurt by well-meaning but unenlightened persons who view their behavior in terms of stubbornness or queerness or perversity rather than in terms of symptoms of an illness beyond the control of the will. Since few neurotic persons find their way into a mental hospital, they are more of a problem to the general physician, clergyman, and other workers in the community.

This discussion of the psychoneuroses has dealt chiefly with the types as distinguished on the basis of symptoms. For a fuller exposition of the character structure of neurotic persons, Horney is valuable to the clergyman and the layman.[16] Her discussion of the relation of anxiety, hostility, and guilt, of the neurotic need for affection, of the urge for power, prestige, and possession in neurotics, of competition and neurotic suffering, are illuminating and emphasize an aspect of the neurotic personality that is usually slighted.

Understanding the neurotic person is especially important for the clergy. The insecurity, instability, and anxiety of many neurotic persons lead them to the church in quest of help. The clergyman may or may not be able to give them much help, but at least he should know what not to do in order to avoid increasing anxiety or deepening their symptoms. He should not, for example, try to get them to give up their symptoms by preachments or arguments. On the other hand, many neurotic persons find the church a convenient channel for the expression of their hostilities. It is not infrequent that such persons gain a position of leadership and influence in a church only to use this position to create trouble. Others may seek to work out their neurosis by influencing or controlling others, and hence seek to teach religion, always under the guise of service. Fostering of neurotic attitudes in the young with the aid of religion may occur in such situations and is indeed detrimental.

CHARACTER DISORDERS

Up to this point we have discussed forms of illness in which the major symptoms involve personality changes. To be sure, such persons show odd and even antisocial behavior. But their behavior is so obviously a manifestation of peculiar personality traits that they are treated, not as criminals but as sick persons. These persons have found it impossible to solve their problems by constructively changing themselves or their environment, in other words, by dealing effectively with reality, internal or external. They have, therefore, found a solution involving changes within themselves which are detrimental to their personalities, detrimental because they avoid rather than include reality. They have suffered personal disintegration in order to escape from an intolerable conflict at some level of integration.

There is another way of dealing with intolerable conflict. This involves destructive changes in the environment rather than in the personality. This method expresses itself in a behavior disorder rather than in a personality change. The major symptoms are some antisocial behavior in a personality which may otherwise appear normal and which manifests none of the usual symptoms of mental illness. Many delinquents and criminals fall in this group, though not all. Some persons become criminal or delinquent because of some constitutional inferiority such as feeble-mindedness. These lack the necessary psychological control of aggressive impulses. Others choose crime as a way of life, quite deliberately and without qualms of conscience. Aggression against society is for them the normal way to live. They become the hardened criminal. Others, however, commit criminal and antisocial acts because the problems of adjustment have produced a character disorder rather than a psychosis or psychoneurosis.

Persons suffering from a character disorder usually receive little understanding from those to whom they are accountable. Many of them, realizing that something is wrong, seek the help of religion to change their lives. Sometimes religion is successful in bringing about a constructive change, but many times it is not. It is indeed regrettable that, for all the long hours spent by clergymen in attempting to help such persons, a method of understanding them and of learning why religion helps some and does not help others has not been developed through pastoral work. This requires skills which theological education has neglected to give to its students.

Character disorders are difficult to discuss briefly because they cover a wide range of human behavior, and because the specific psychological factors involved may vary greatly from case to case. [19] All of them, however, have one element in common—the presence of a great deal of aggression and hostility which is turned against other people in one way or another. Sometimes it is directed toward specific persons, or toward certain kinds of persons, such as members of the opposite or the same sex, or persons in authority, or toward society in general. Paradoxical as it may sound, some hostility grows out of a sense of guilt which demands punishment. The antisocial act is the person's way of bringing punishment on himself in order to assuage his guilt.

In general it may be said that character disorders are the result of the individual's failure to deal with the painful realities of experience in ways that make for growth and adaptation to the social group. As the result of this failure, hostility created by his suffering is turned on some aspect of his environment. His way of life is one of rebellion. But this rebellion is not of his conscious choosing. It is the expression of impulses he has neither the power to eradicate from his personality nor the strength to control. On the whole, society condemns him for being different, when it should accept a part of the responsibility for his failure. He is in need of cure, not condemnation or punishment.

MENTAL ILLNESS AND ORGANISM-ENVIRONMENT RELATIONSHIPS

This discussion of the emotional factor in mental illness is, of course, simplified, and has necessarily neglected many of the complex and difficult technical problems involved. However, it should be clear that mental illness, like physical illness, is not so much a specific disease of a particular organ as the reaction of the total personality to complex environmental relationships which create tension and hinder growth. Physical factors make these adjustments more or less difficult or impossible, depending on their nature, severity, and the way the person deals with them. Physical incapacities such as deafness or lameness may become a basis for unhealthy personality patterns which, in their end result, may be no less serious than personality changes created by syphilis. But it should be noted that such physical factors do not directly cause mental illness. It is the psychological reaction of the total person to these and other life experiences that leads either to illness or to health.

Cultural factors are of greater significance in mental illness than has yet been generally recognized. We venture the assertion that, if this aspect of mental illness were to be as throughly investigated through research as have been certain physical factors, a long step would be taken in both prevention and treatment. But in addition to this, a great many facts would be revealed about our culture that many people would prefer to keep hidden from view. In the values, patterns, and pressures of the culture, as these operate to influence personality attitudes, ideas and reactions, lie crucial problems involving the health of the personality. Religion, being both an individual experience and a cultural phenomenon, may play a major role in producing and intensifying individual and cultural conflicts and reactions which lead to illness or it may provide a basis for the healthy solution of conflicts and the achievement of creative personal and social patterns. Illness, health, and religion alike are rooted in the relationships of the organism within itself and with its environment.

REFERENCES

1. DEVINE, HENRY, *Recent Advances in Psychiatry,* 2nd Ed., p. 284. Philadelphia, 1933.
2. STRECKER, EDWARD A., and EBAUGH, FRANKLIN G., *Practical Clinical Psychiatry,* 5th Ed. Philadelphia, 1940.
   BROWN, J. F., *The Psychodynamics of Abnormal Behavior.* New York, 1940.
   HENDERSON, D. K., and GILLESPIE, R. B., *Textbook of Psychiatry,* 5th Ed. New York, 1940.
3. The Annual Report of the Commissioner of Mental Health of the Commonwealth of Massachusetts for the year ending Nov. 30, 1939, p. 169.
4. WHITE, WILLIAM A., *Medical Psychology,* p. 113. New York, 1931.
5. SELIGER, R. V., "The problem of the alcoholic in the community," *American Journal of Psychiatry,* 95: 1938, p. 701.
6. FREUD, S., *Collected Papers,* Vol. 3, p. 390. London, 1925.
7. Dayton found this to be 122 out of every 100,000 of the population in the age group of 40-69 during the period of 1917-1933. See DAYTON, NEIL, *New Facts on Mental Disorder,* p. 313. Baltimore, 1940.
8. MALAMUD, WILLIAM, "Mental Disorders of the Aged," to be published in United States Public Health Service Bulletin.

9. DUBLIN, LOUIS, I., "Longevity in Retrospect and Prospect," in *Problems of Ageing*, p. 100. Edited by E. V. Cowdry. Baltimore, 1939.

10. The Annual Report of the Commissioner of Mental Health of the Commonwealth of Massachusetts for the year ending Nov. 30, 1939, p. 323.

11. See United States Bureau of Census, *Patients in Hospitals for Mental Disease*, 1937.

12. DAYTON, NEIL A., *New Facts on Mental Disorder*, p. 283. Baltimore, 1940.

13. MALAMUD, WILLIAM, "Mental Disorders of the Aged," to be published in United States Public Health Service Bulletin.

14. ROTHSCHILD, D., "Pathologic changes in senile psychoses and their psychobiologic significance," *American Journal of Psychiatry*, 93: 1937, p. 757.

15. MILES, WALTER R., "Psychological Aspects of Ageing," in *Problems of Ageing*, p. 535. Edited by E. V. Cowdry. Baltimore, 1939.

16. HORNEY, K., *The Neurotic Personality of Our Time*. New York, 1937.

17. For example, by Horney, above, and KARDINER, A., *The Individual and His Society*. New York, 1939.

18. HENDERSON, D. K., and GILLESPIE, R. B., *Textbook of Psychiatry*, 5th Ed., Chap. 15. New York, 1940.

19. Reader is referred to MENNINGER, KARL A., *Man Against Himself* (New York, 1938) and BROWN, J. F., *Psychodynamics of Abnormal Behavior* (New York, 1940).

CHAPTER IV

FUNDAMENTAL PRINCIPLES OF THE ORGANISMIC APPROACH

SCIENCE cannot develop without basic concepts which organize and interpret the multitude of facts it accumulates. The early Greeks understood that basic to the science of medicine was the conception of man held by the physician. In this chapter we shall discuss certain basic concepts through which the organismic view of man is formulated.[1] This is in anticipation of the consideration of religion in illness and health from the point of view of organism environment relationships.

THE FUNCTION OF INTEGRATION

Central in the organismic approach is the principle that the organism is more than the mathematical sum of its parts and that "the organism in its totality is as essential to an explanation of its elements as its elements are to an explanation of the organism."[2] The analytic study of the various parts of the organism reveals the function that they serve in relation to the whole. It does not, however, reveal the function that is served by the organism as a whole. This function is, at least in part, that of uniting the various organs into a unity which makes their functioning possible. It is this function of integration which makes the organism more than the mathematical sum of its parts. It is essential for the creation of a living whole, which remains alive only because of the necessary organization of its parts.

Integration is not a function added to the parts, but one which controls the parts and relates them together in a totality. Parts are created by and exist for the whole organism;

64

the organism does not exist for the parts. As a botanist, De-Bary has said: "Plants make the cells, not the cells plants." Neither the whole nor the parts can enjoy a separate existence. They exist only as different aspects of an organic unity. In regard to this function of integration, one worker writes: "The only real unity is that of the organism, and as long as its cells remain in continuity they are to be regarded, not as morphological individuals, but as specialized centers of action into which the living body resolves itself, and by means of which the physiological division of labor is effected."[3]

The organism not only has a function, it also has a structure. This structure may be viewed in a static manner after the fashion of anatomy or it may be seen in relation to the dynamic function of integration. It is this function which is necessary to explain the orderly arrangement of the various parts of the organism into a whole. This orderly arrangement we call structure. It is through the structure that the integration takes place. The two cannot be separated; without one there could not be the other. Their close relationship may be expressed in the statement that structure is organized function.

This principle may be illustrated by an example taken from the work of Child.[4] A part of undifferentiated protoplasm may be stimulated at a given point by its movement in water. The result of this stimulation is an increase in activity resulting in a greater expenditure of energy at the point of stimulation. This increase of energy output, however, is not confined to the point stimulated, but spreads throughout the organism, diminishing gradually as it recedes from the point of stimulation. An analogy is the series of waves produced when a stone is thrown into a quiet pool. Growth of cells takes place more rapidly where the exchange of energy is highest. In this way a pattern of development is established—the dynamic gradient, or axis. A stimulus that is long continued, often repeated, or very strong tends in proportion to establish permanent changes in the protoplasm, and the gradient becomes permanently structuralized.

The point of stimulation is, in this manner, developed into the head of the organism, the opposite end becoming the tail. This very sketchy outline serves to illustrate how structure is organized in function, or how function becomes structuralized in physiological processes.

Another illustration of a different kind may be given. An individual in a given situation acts in a certain way in order to adjust himself to some environmental stimulus. The stimulus is repeated, and an habitual way of acting or reacting is established. In this case, the habit is a psychological structure which results from the behavior of the organism. This behavior serves a function within the organism. The habit is, therefore, to be looked upon as the structuralization of function.

Function and structure, then, are to be considered as two inseparable aspects of the same living process, not as separate or contradictory aspects. Function can take place only through a structure, be that structure chemical, physical, psychological, or social. The organism as a whole is always seeking certain ends, and the structure serves as a means to these ends. One of these ends is integration. As a worker in the field of embryology concludes: "Comparative embryology reminds us at every turn that the organism dominates cell-formation, using for the same purpose one, several or many cells, massing its material, and directing its movements, and shaping its organs, as if cells did not exist, or as if they existed only in complete subordination to its will, if I may so speak."[5] In other words, structure is organized function. The individual is organized in a way that integrates all its parts under the domination of the function which we call mind.

THE FUNCTION OF INDIVIDUATION

There is another aspect of the life of the organism closely related to integration and structuralization. It is the function of individuation. The essence of individuation may be summed up in the statement that no two persons are exactly alike; they have similarities, but also differences which mark them as distinct individuals. The illustration used above, the description of a bit of protoplasm developing structure also illustrates the process of individuation. Before the developing of structure it was just another mass of protoplasm; after the development of structure it was a distinct organism. Not only in protoplasm, but in the higher forms of life, this tendency to individuation is clear, resulting first in species, then in subspecies, with final consummation in individual differences which in man are very pronounced.

Individuation, like integration, is a function of the organism as a whole, not of any part. It is also closely related to the function of integration. The nature of this relationship has been a problem for science, and one on which new light has been thrown. Individuation, in so far as the internal life of the organism is concerned, has to do with the development of functions by separate parts of the organism. Thus we do not digest food with our whole organism; we digest it with our stomachs. Likewise, the function of walking is centered in the limbs. A reflex is a function of the nervous system. It has been a prevailing view that the development of the partial pattern, such as the reflex, came first, and was later integrated into the total individual through experience. Thus learning to walk was considered to take place through association of many simple activities of the nervous system through which the complex activity was achieved. The mind was thought of as a mosaic of learned habits or patterns of behavior. Elaborate theories of education were erected on this view.

The work of G. E. Coghill in research on Amblystoma has produced findings quite the opposite of this view. The older view held that individuation preceded integration; that an individual learned to do something, then the newly learned habit was built into the structure of the nervous system. Coghill's evidence leads him to the conclusion that the organism functions as a whole throughout its development. In other words, integration is a basic characteristic of the growing organism, not a result. Individuation, or the development of partial patterns of behavior, such as walking, depends on the functioning of the organism as a whole. He writes: "The neural mechanism, while affecting integration in the older muscles, is growing into the younger, non-functional muscles, so that when the latter becomes sensitive to neural excitation they are in perfect integration with the total functioning system."[6] Thus when any part of the organism, such as the leg or eye muscles, begins its specific functions, "they must find themselves integrated with the total organismic pattern. . . . They are primarily and fundamentally a part of the total pattern from the first. Their relative individuation is a secondary acquisition." Thus growth takes place not through trial-and-error learning, but in accordance with the "laws of growth within the nervous system. . . . The nervous system, while functioning in the performance of one pattern is through growth elaborating the neural counterpart of another."

The relationship of the organism and the environment has already been touched in regard to structuralization. There it was seen that the environmental stimulus is a definite factor in the development of structure and, therefore, individuation. The problem is, to what extent is the organism at the mercy of the environment?

The work of Coghill throws light on this problem by describing the development of the nervous system. He discovered that the parts of the nervous system through which the organism acts on its environment develop before those parts through which the organism gets impressions and stimulation from the environment and on the basis of which it reacts to the environment. Coghill is, therefore, able to state specifically that "the individual acts on its environment before it reacts to its environment."[7]

The fact that the individual acts on the environment before it reacts to the environment means that such actions are stimulated by processes or needs within the organism itself. "Behavior in response to such stimulation is spontaneous in the sense that it is the expression of the intrinsic dynamics of the organism as a whole."[8] Furthermore, the activity of a part of the organism is controlled by the total pattern unless some abnormality exists. "The mechanism of the total pattern is an essential component of the performance of the part."

It is through this subordination of the parts to the whole that the organism is capable of making those adjustments to its environment which are essential to the continuance of its life and for its growth. In making these adjustments the organism remains capable of modifying its environment and of acting spontaneously and on its own initiative. Coghill writes: "Insofar as the correlation of nervous structure and function in the development of the individual has been carried, structural provision has been found for the perpetuation of spontaneity, autonomy or initiative as a factor in its behavior. Any theory of motivation, therefore, that attributes this function wholly to the environment, is grossly inadequate."[8]

This point of view discovers within the individual organism qualities of initiative and originality which the older mosaic conception cast out as "unscientific." It is to be borne in mind, however, that the older conception was based entirely on the method of analysis, and "analysis alone is incapable of interpreting, or understanding organic beings. No natural object which in its nature is more distinctively synthetic than analytic can be understood by knowledge-processes which are more analytic than synthetic."[9] The organism as a whole has functions not discoverable in any of its parts. Coghill maintains that his work has placed the conception of the organism as a whole and the total behavior pattern "positively within the scientific realm, as opposed to the hypothetical or vitalistic."[10]

TENSION AND EQUILIBRIUM

We shall return later to a further consideration of the relationship between the organism and the environment. At this point it is desirable to discuss two closely related concepts, those of tension and equilibrium. These concepts represent different aspects of an experience that is central in all nature and in the life of every organism. The constant endeavor to reduce tensions and to gain equilibrium makes the difference between a static, lifeless object and a dynamic, moving organism.

By a state of tension we mean a disturbance within the organism, caused by either inner or external factors, or a combination, which propels the organism toward a goal or a kind of behavior that is aimed at removing or reducing the disturbance. The state of relative quiet or balance or harmony thus achieved is called equilibrium. Pain of any kind is a tension, as is hunger. Equilibrium is restored when the pain is lessened or removed or the hunger appeased.

These concepts are fundamental to an understanding of the dynamic forces of nature. They imply that within the organism there are forces working in opposite directions. Thus the wind causes a tree to sway in proportion to the strength of the wind, but within the tree there are forces which constantly bring it back to its original position. Our illustration of the protoplasm stimulated by the movement in water is also pertinent. The stimulation set up tensions in the form of increased energy at certain points. This increased energy brought certain definite reactions from protoplasm as a means of re-establishing a condition of harmony or equilibrium. These reactions, aimed at the integration of the protoplasm, resulted in a definite structure. It is well known that animals in cold regions develop thick coats of fur as a means of offsetting the cold and retaining heat; that a bit of dirt in the eye brings forth tears in an attempt to remove the irritating factor; and that an infection in any part of the body sets up counteracting processes. Students of dynamic psychology have uncovered numerous psychological processes through which tension is released and equilibrium is restored, at least, in consciousness. The symptoms presented by the neurotic person, for example, may be interpreted as unhealthy attempts to reduce inner tension, or at least to keep it from consciousness.

This constant endeavor on the part of the living organism to reduce tensions and re-establish an equilibrium has been noted by investigators in various fields. Fredericq, a physiologist, expressed it thus: "A living being is adjusted in such a manner that each perturbing influence provokes to activity a compensating apparatus which brings about its neutralization and the repair of the damage."[11] Cannon, on the basis of years of physiological research, concludes that within the organism there are physical and chemical processes which serve the one purpose of maintaining a state of constancy or equilibrium, to which state he gives the name "homeostasis."[12] He says: "The coordinated physiological processes which maintain most of the steady states in the organism are so complex and so peculiar to living beings—involving, as they may, the brain and nerves, the heart, lungs, kidneys and spleen, all working cooperatively that I have suggested a special designation of these states, homeostasis. The word does not imply something set and immobile, a stagnation. It means a condition—a condition which may vary, but which is relatively constant." Cannon's book is an elaboration of this theme, and shows how the organism meets situations of a disturbing nature and maintains a certain stability of both materials, such as water and sugar, and of processes, such as heat regulation. Fundamental in the preservation of this state of constancy or equilibrium is the activity of the autonomic and sympathetic nervous systems. The organism is equipped through these systems to meet disturbances or tensions arising either from within the organism or from the environment, and to maintain an equilibrium which is necessary to the life of the organism.

On the psychological level the experience of emotional tension is a commonplace event. Fear, for example, is a tension that leads to activities calculated to produce safety and hence re-establish equilibrium; anger, love, and pain are similar tensions leading to appropriate activities, appropriate because they reduce tension. A desire of any kind is a state of tension motivating the person in the direction of activity that will bring satisfaction. The symptoms of illness may be understood as attempts on the part of the organism to reduce tensions and to gain equilibrium that are inappropriate and unhealthy because they employ psychological and physiological processes which interfere with continued integration and growth of the individual.

From the physiological point of view, Cannon formulated the concept of homeostasis. From the psychoanalytical point of view, Freud arrived at a conclusion strikingly similar, and which he terms the pleasure principle. By this principle is meant the tendency of psychic life to seek pleasure and avoid pain; in other words, the constant need and endeavor to reduce emotional tensions.[13] Stated positively, it would mean that there is a disposition on the part of the organism to initiate psychological processes for the purpose of restoring the equilibrium. Restoration of equilibrium is psychologically perceived as pleasure.

The establishment of equilibrium within the organism is closely related to the functions of integration and individuation. A state of tension is always a challenge to the organism to neutralize the disturbance in one way or another. This involves both integration and individuation. The life of the organism and its growth demands not only the reduction of tensions but reduction in a way that is detrimental to neither life nor growth. A disease symptom may be understood in this sense. Thus a fever may be the attempt to rid the organism of an infectious germ that has intruded, and is hampering the physiological functioning. Or a mental symptom such as a delusion may be an attempt to rid the organism, at least consciousness, of a tension in the form of anxiety.

But here anxiety is analogous to the fever, not the infection. For anxiety, like fever, has an underlying causative factor that is to be sought either in the relationships of the organism within itself (such as a conflict between an impulse and conscience) or between the organism and its environment. In either case, the well-being of the organism is at stake. Health requires a solution that creates new integration and structure. Equilibrium may be established in a way that promotes or that prevents growth. Here the function of individuality is at stake, for this is to be achieved only through growth according to the laws of the organism. Tension may also be a sign of the failure of integration. Thus a recalcitrant gland, which is not functioning under the control of the organism as a whole, will create tensions having physiological and psychological consequences. Likewise, an experience running counter to an individual's ideals may create serious tensions. The significance of tension and equilibrium on the psychological, social, and religious levels will be dealt with more fully later.

VARIOUS LEVELS OF THE LIFE OF THE ORGANISM

Thus far we have talked about the organism as a whole and we have referred to various aspects of the life of the organism, such as the physical and the psychological. The relation of these various aspects to each other and to the organism needs now to be clarified.

A living organism may be viewed in terms of different levels on which its life finds expression, or on which the functions of integration, structuralization, and individuation may be carried out. These levels may be characterized as the chemical, physiological, psychological, and social.

The relation of these levels may be illustrated by a concrete situation. The need for satisfaction, sexual satisfaction, for example, may be approached from any of these various levels. It has its chemical component arising from the secretion of certain endocrine glands. Its physiological component is to be found in the tension within the sexual organs and their readiness for activity. The psychological component is somewhat more complex. First, there is the feeling or the impulse which translates itself in terms of the idea of gratification. This idea may be of various kinds, autoerotic, homosexual, or heterosexual, depending on many factors, particularly the psychological. In addition, there is the evaluation of this idea by another psychological component, commonly called conscience. This in turn may lead to a repression of the impulse and idea, or to its direct expression or to some substitute expression or sublimation. But this evaluation and control by conscience introduces another level of life, the social. It is from the person's social and cultural environment that the specific character of his conscience is derived. In addition to its influence on conscience, cultural factors may enter into sex expression in other ways. Thus a person who might not be deterred by his conscience may be deterred by certain social pressures. Or a person who is deterred by his conscience may be influenced toward expression by other social influences.

This illustration will serve to emphasize the fact that the organism functions as a whole, even though, for purposes of analysis, various levels of functioning may be distinguished. Furthermore, an experience can never be thoroughly understood until it is understood on all levels. Explanation may be made only in terms of the same level or of a higher level. Thus physiological facts cannot be adequately explained in terms of chemical facts, as on the physiological level other factors are added. Likewise, psychological facts can be adequately explained only on the psychological or social level, never on the physical level. Again, social integration cannot be adequately explained on the physiological or psychological level. Each level involves additional factors and therefore cannot be adequately explained in terms of a lower level. It cannot be overemphasized that these levels are but aspects of the functioning of the organism as a whole.

The fact that the life of the organism finds expression on

various levels is significant for the functions of integration and individuation. Each level may be thought of as presenting areas of integration or as a means through which the organism differentiates itself from other organisms. Thus we speak of chemical integrations, physiological integrations, psychological and social integrations. "The same laws hold for the manifestations of reactions" on each of these levels.[14] In other words, in a personality in which there is a strong compensatory reaction on the psychological level, a similar reaction will be found on the chemical and physiological levels. A failure to find integration on one level will disturb integrations on other levels. Tensions arising on one level will present problems of integration on other levels. Thus a psychological conflict may have either physiological or social effects that disturb the integrations on those levels. An example of this is the boy who is in conflict and who, therefore, becomes a behavior problem. Again, however, we come back to the insistence of the investigators that the organism functions as a whole and that mental processes are the dominant factors in the total integration. As White says: "All the organic functioning parts of the human organism are related and find their final and highest expression in symbolic patterns which set forth the tendencies of the organism-as-a-whole in what are called psychological terms."[15]

THE RELATION OF THE ORGANISM TO THE ENVIRONMENT

In our introductory chapter and throughout this chapter, there have been frequent references to the relation of the organism to the environment. This relationship needs more elaboration.

Fundamental to the life of the organism is the fact that it lives in an environment. This environment at once provides elements essential to the life of the organism and also elements detrimental to it. The example of the protoplasm indicates the dynamic possibilities in the organism-environment relationship.

Cannon holds that the environment of the organism is not only the world external to it, but that it also has an internal environment. He points out the fact that the organism is separated from the atmosphere surrounding it by a layer of dead cells (skin) or by a film of mucous or of salt solution. "All that is alive within these lifeless surfaces is immersed in the fluids of the body, the blood and the lymph, which form an internal environment."[16] He indicates how changes within this internal environment may create dangers for the organism, and that the organism is equipped with various processes which tend to neutralize these dangers. Thus integration and homeostasis is secured in part through the internal environment, through the blood and tissue fluids. The environment, therefore, is quite essential to the integration and growth of the organism. J. S. Haldane, discussing the same problem from the point of view of the physiology of breathing, comes to the conclusion that we cannot speak in terms of "a mere definitely bounded physical structure, nor of the activity of such a structure. An organism is one with its environment both internal and external."[17]

It may be said that there is no part of the environment which does not have some significance for the organism. Cosmic and geographic conditions, air, water, light, heat, food, materials harmful to the organism, such as poisons and bacteria, other persons, social, economic, cultural and religious conditions or atmosphere—all these, and perhaps others which have been omitted, are significant. One student of the problem writes: "It is important to realize that to reach a region of events entirely irrelevant to the organism, one has to go far afield, in fact, outside the solar system. Within the region of events that are relevant to the organism the distinction betwen organism and environment is not a sharp one."[18]

The environment influences the organism on each of the various levels, chemical, physiological, psychological and social. Changes in the amount of oxygen available for consumption initiate chemical changes having profound effects on the psychologcial processes and on the entire organism. The environment may stimulate the organism psychologically in such a manner as will create profound tensions, which in turn lead to physical or chemical changes such as is produced in the experience of sudden fright, where changes in heart rate, blood presure, and the discharge of adrenalin take place. "The organism is a highly integrated unit and responds with subtle changes at many levels to the various demands made upon it at any one level; the stress of a psychological situation mobilizes complicated biochemical and physiological processes, while changes in the chemical interchange between organism and environment may influence emotions, alter the direction of thought, modify the code of values."[19]

The relationship between the organism and the environment may be further considered in terms of the vital need of the organism for energy. Man, as a living organism, "captures his energy from the cosmic energy of the known universe, transforms it, and then discharges it in function; be that metabolic, reflex action, or human behavior."[19] This capture of energy takes place through the utilization within the organism of elements from the environment and the release of energy takes place in terms of behavior directed toward the environment. "Living now becomes, not a special series of processes of the individual organs, but a series of interactions between the individual and the environment, in which the environment supplies the energy, man the means of capturing it, transforming it, and releasing it."[20] It should be noted in passing that this capture and release of energy takes place on all levels of the life of the organism. Here again the organism functions as a whole, and events on one level are significant for each level.

The environment has a profound effect on the life of the organism; but the organism also profoundly affects the environment. Here we should refer back to the work of Coghill, which shows definitely that the organism acts on the environment before it reacts to it, and that throughout the life of the organism it retains a measure of spontaneity and initiative. Especially is this true of the human being. Examples could be multiplied of the way in which human beings endeavor and succeed in altering some aspect of their physical or cultural environment, or of adapting that environment to themselves. The efforts of science might be reviewed in this light. Those acquainted with the behavior of neurotic and psychotic persons know the various ways in which they seek to control the environment for their own purposes. These purposes may be antisocial or destructive, or merely annoying to others, but the principle holds. Sometimes physical illness is to be understood in part as an attempt to control the environment for selfish purposes. Persons who are not ill may do the same to a lesser degree. Many social reform movements have as their manifest purpose the altering of something in the cultural environment. Religion, at least Christianity, has always taught that the person may and should exert some control over his environment in the interest of ideal values.

On the psychological level, there is another important aspect of this relationship between the individual and his environment. Psychiatrists and psychoanalysts particularly have been pointing out that the environment itself is not so significant psychologically as is the person's interpretation of that environment. Freud and his followers have emphasized this point, as have others. A person's interpretation of his environment is the result of complex processes including many past events and their interpretations, conscious and unconscious attitudes, and conscious and unconscious aims of the individual. Thus the relationship between a teacher and a group of children may be different in the case of each child, because each child places a different interpretation on the behavior of the teacher. This coincides with the conclusions of Coghill; indeed, it is almost a restatement on the psychological level of his findings on the physiological level. It is this individual bias which accounts for the various interpretations which different persons make of the same event or aspect of reality, and it is to be found quite as much among average adults, scientists, philosophers, and religionists as among children. The fantastic interpretations which many psychotic persons make of their world is another illustration. Thus a certain kind of patient will interpret a trivial act on the part of another person as meaning that he is being persecuted.

The problems involved in the relationship between the individual and his world are receiving much study today from various scientific disciplines. It is to Freud and his followers that credit must be given for a major contribution in the understanding of the relationships on the psychological level. However, psychiatrists of various schools of thought are centering their attention on this problem. This is undoubtedly because of the nature of mental illness, which always involves the person's relationships to his environment. One psychiatrist defines the province of psychiatry as the area of "inter-personal relationships," indicating that it is the relationship of man to man that is highly important in the study of mental illness.[21] This would be equally true in many cases where the symptoms of illness are physical, but their underlying cause is emotional.

A different but highly valuable approach to organism-environment relationships is being made by the cultural anthropologists.[22] This group is particularly interested in the influence of the culture, defined in terms of the total structure of society, upon the individual personality. Comparative studies of cultures are especially enlightening. The work of this group is of increasing significance for both medicine and religion.

The principles discussed in this chapter have an important bearing on the concept of health and illness. To the extent that the organism functions as a whole it may be said to be in a state of health. Functioning as a whole implies integration of its various parts, as well as the growth of the parts under the control of the whole. Illness arises when, for whatever reason, integration breaks down and the part gains control over the whole. Thus an organism may be dominated by the faulty functioning of an anatomical part, such as the heart, or a psychological part, such as a feeling of anxiety or an inadequate belief. Or it may be dominated by some part of its environment, such as a disease germ or a severe, cruel parent. In any case, the organism ceases to function as a whole. Behind any specific manifestation of illness there lies a period of conflict and tension, and an unsuccessful attempt on the part of the organism to regain its equilibrium and bring its parts under the control of the whole. To be healthy is not only to be free of anxiety, but it is also to be whole.

REFERENCES

1. An illuminating discussion of organism environment relationships has appeared since this chapter was written. See ANDRAS ANGYAL, *Foundations for a Science of Personality*. New York, 1941.
2. RITTER, W. E., *The Unity of the Organism*, 1919, quoted by WHITE, W. A., *Psychoanalytic Review,* 7: 1920, pp. 71-78.
3. WILSON, E. B., quoted by DUNBAR, F., *Emotions and Bodily Changes,* p. 9. New York, 1935.
4. CHILD, C. M., *Individuality in Organism*. Chicago, 1915.
5. WHITMAN, C. O., quoted by DUNBAR, F., *Emotions and Bodily Changes,* p. 9. New York, 1935.
6. COGHILL, G. E., "The mechanism of integration in Amblystoma punctatum," *Journal of Comparative Neurology,* 41: 1926, pp. 95-152.
7. COGHILL, G. E., "The mechanism of association of Amblystoma punctatum," *Journal of Comparative Neurology,* 51: 1930, pp. 311-375.
8. COGHILL, G. E., "Corollaries of the anatomical and physiological study of Amblystoma punctatum from the earliest movement to swimming," *Journal of Comparative Neurology,* 53: 1931, pp. 147-168.
9. RITTER, W. E., quoted by WHITE, W. A., *Medical Psychology,* p. 17. New York, 1931.
10. COGHILL, G. E., "Corollaries of the anatomical and physiological study of Amblystoma punctatum from the earliest

movement to swimming," *Journal of Comparative Neurology*, 53: 1931, pp. 147-168.

11. Quoted by WHITE, W. A., *Medical Psychology*, p. 28. New York, 1931.

12. CANNON, WALTER B., *The Wisdom of the Body*, p. 24. New York, 1932.

13. See HENDRICK, IVES, *Facts and Theories of Psychoanalysis*, pp. 92-98. New York, 1934.

14. WHITE, W. A., "Social significance in mental disease," *Archives of Neurology & Psychiatry*, 22: 1929, pp. 873-900.

15. WHITE, W. A., *Medical Psychology*, p. 31. New York, 1931.

16. CANNON, WALTER B., *Wisdom of the Body*, p. 263. New York, 1932.

17. HALDANE, J. S., *Organism and Environment as Illustrated by the Physiology of Breathing*, 1917, quoted by DUNBAR, H. F., *Emotions and Bodily Changes*, p. 52. New York, 1935.

18. RICHIE, A. D., "The relations of mental and physical processes," *Mind*, 40: 1931, pp. 171-187.

19. CAMPBELL, C. M., *The Human Personality and the Environment*, p. 5. New York, 1934.

20. JELLIFFE, S. E., "The epileptic attack in dynamic pathology," *New York Medical Journal*, 108: 1918, pp. 139-143.

21. SULLIVAN, H. S., "Conceptions of modern psychiatry," *Psychiatry*, 1: 1938, pp. 121-134.

22. See, for example, *The Individual and His Society*, by A. Kardiner (New York, 1939); *The Study of Man*, by Ralph Linton (New York, 1936); *Patterns of Culture*, by Ruth Benedict (Boston, 1934); and *Sex and Temperament*, by Margaret Mead (New York, 1935).

CHAPTER V

PERSONALITY IN ILLNESS AND HEALTH

PERSONALITY is a much used and abused word. It is defined in terms ranging from the superficiality of cosmetics to the profundities of metaphysics.[1] In this chapter we shall attempt to arrive at a concept of personality that is intellectually tenable and practically useful. We shall also discuss problems bearing on the relation of personality to illness and health, and shall introduce considerations bearing on religion and personality.

THE MEANING OF PERSONALITY

Thus far we have presented a point of view that has gained rapid acceptance in medicine during the past several decades. Briefly stated, this point of view looks upon the individual as an organism rather than a mechanism, an organism in which there is a basic unity not contributed by its parts but rather inherent in the nature of the organism itself; an organism capable of growth and individuation within certain limits imposed by its need for unity or integration; an organism in which chemical, physical, and psychological mechanisms are present but which in the state of health are dominated by the organism as a whole. Mechanisms are important structures through which the organism achieves its ends, but they do not explain the organism. Mechanisms of various kinds play an important part in illness, but they are not to be confused with the cause of the illness. The close relationship existing between the organism and its environment has been stressed, and we have seen that there is a sense in which it is true that the organism is one with its environment, that its life is dependent upon an interaction of forces and proc-

esses within the organism and within the environment.
Health has been defined as a state in which the organism as
a whole is in control of its parts and illness as a condition in
which the parts are controlling the activities of the organism
as a whole.

Personality, as we are thinking of it, is the manifestation
of the life of the organism in its totality. We cannot think of
personality as we think of an organ, such as the stomach.
Personality is rather the expression, in social relations, of the
total life processes and experiences of the organism. In clinical experience and in life, personality is never found apart
from a living organism and it is always the expression of
what has happened within the organism and what at the
moment is happening.

It is misleading to think of personality as being more the
expression of one part of the organism than of another. This
leads inevitably to a one-sided emphasis which neglects other
equally important aspects. Everything that occurs on any
level of life is of significance to the personality. An endocrine
disturbance, a physical injury, an experience resulting in joy
or sorrow, a social situation that is satisfying or frustrating,
alike have their influence on personality. In a given person
at a given time experience on one level may be having more
than its proper influence, and to the extent that this is true
the individual is ill. Illnesses involving either physical or
mental symptoms result in a change in personality, the chief
difference being one of degree, mental symptoms involving
the greater change. Physicians as a group have been too much
concerned with the physical side of their patients, to the
neglect of other just as important aspects. On the other hand,
clergymen have been too much concerned with the spiritual
side, to the neglect of the physical and sometimes also of the
psychological and the social. We are learning today that these
are inseparably related, and that personality can best be
served only when this relationship is recognized.

The central problem of personality in our culture at least
is that of interpersonal relationships. It is out of these rela-

tionships that the deepest satisfactions and the most acute frustrations are experienced. It should not be surprising that here also are to be found the most fundamental problems for both religion and health.

The relationships between an individual and his world serve the highly significant functions of providing those values essential to the life and growth of the personality as a whole. By a value we mean anything which satisfies a need of the personality. Food, friendship, and fresh air are values, because they satisfy needs. We shall not attempt to classify human values according to any theory in regard to lesser or greater values. Every person is different, and trying to fit personalities into a hard and fast system of values may do much harm and even lead to illness. For some people fresh air and food may be more important at times than friendship, though many want to enjoy all three at the same time. Lack of sufficient oxygen or proper food may be just as devastating to the personality as lack of friends. Haldane describes the effects on the personality accompanying a decreased supply of oxygen.[2] The senses and the intellect become dulled without the person becoming aware of it, the power of the memory is quickly affected and finally almost entirely annulled. The ability to make sane judgments is much impaired, and the person becomes subject to irrational fixed ideas and to uncontrolled emotional outbursts. It is important to remember that just as serious changes are produced by conflicts in the level of personal relationships, and that in our culture more persons are being made ill by a frustration of love and affection than by a lack of fresh air. One of our major problems today is to develop a culture in which persons may experience those values which are essential to health.

Mention of food, friendship, and fresh air raises the further problem as to the relation of values to the personality as a whole. It is very easy to be analytical in our thinking, and to remain analytical, and we are suffering today from an undue tendency to think of men in analytical terms rather than as a whole. We miss an important aspect of personality if we think of values as remaining on the level on which they originate. In other words, there are no part-personality values; there are only values of the personality as a whole. Fresh air is often thought of as a simple physical value. It originates on that level. It satisfies needs which arise on that level. But unless those needs are satisfied the entire personality is changed. Through the physical medium the individual experiences values essential to the personality as a whole.

Food is more complicated. There are no social or moral restrictions on the use of fresh air, but sometimes this is controlled by economic circumstances. In food we have an illustration of a value that is basically physical yet has become the center of many social restrictions and customs. Our food must be obtained in a certain way; we must eat it in a certain manner. To the value of physical nourishment there are added social values and a person may be judged by his table manners. Food may become symbolic of other values, and we may eat not because we need the food physically, but because emotional satisfactions are derived from eating. Psychoanalysts point out that conflicts engendered at the weaning stage have serious consequences for the later development of personality. To the small child food and love are closely identified, and eating problems in early childhood result from emotional conflict with the parents. The great vogue which smoking, chewing gum, drinking, and overeating enjoy in our culture should at least make us suspicious of the value of oral gratification apart from physical nourishment. Food is indeed a value for the personality as a whole.

Friendship is not so simple a value as food. It originates not on one level, but on a combination of the physical, psychological, and social. It satisfies many needs of the personality. In a few persons, the capacity for friendship is controlled by physical conditions. One example of this is the small percentage of homosexuals in whom a constitutional factor is responsible for their plight. For most persons, the capacity for friendship is controlled by psychological factors and is directly related to the level of emotional growth that has been achieved. Thus some adults experience friendship as a relationship of more or less complete dependency, seeking to get all they can from their friends and to give nothing in return. To others, a friend is a person whom one eventually hurts, even as Wilde wrote that "each man kills the thing he loves."[3] This is true of certain kinds of persons who cannot love without also hating. In other persons, the capacity for friendship is inhibited by anxiety and hostility. These are very lonely folk, who feel unhappy and have a strong sense of deprivation. The mature person is emotionally able to meet others in a give-and-take relationship, enjoying others for what they are and willing to be enjoyed for what he is.

We have chosen the value of friendship for this discussion because it is a common illustration of interpersonal relationships. The way in which a given person works out this relationship depends largely on the experiences he has had in those basic interpersonal relations with his parents. Thus the capacity for friendship is the result of complex and deep experiences. In turn, friendship serves complex and deep values within the total personality. Tensions arising from failure in such interpersonal relations may upset the equilibrium of the entire personality, and along with tensions from other sources, lead to illness. Friendship is a value, not for any part of the personality, but for the personality as a whole.

We have stressed the relation of values to personality partially in preparation for the consideration of religion as an experience of meaning and value. There is, however, another reason for stressing this. A value is the objective counterpart of the subjective need of the person. For our purposes we may define a need as a state of tension that propels the organism to search for situations which will create equilibrium or to avoid situations which will create more tension. Thus needs are not to be confused with the older concept of instincts, which is no longer tenable. A need may develop on any level of the organism but, once felt, the individual as a whole seeks its satisfaction. It may rise out of deep elements of the personality, such as the need for love, or out of more superficial elements, such as the need of a person to own a bigger car than his neighbor.

Understanding the needs of personality leads to the very heart of human activity, for it reveals the dynamic forces which make people what they are. Ultimately the problems of illness and health and the problems of religion and salvation come back to the needs of personality, and the manner in which these needs are satisfied or frustrated. A culture or a religion which, on the one hand, fails to place personality needs in a central position, subordinating other needs to them, and which, on the other, fails to give the individual a superpersonal goal involving the satisfaction of personality needs by and for a group, cannot fail to produce the rising tide of illness, crime, and social catastrophe which we are facing today. The needs of personality are the common center out of which man's deepest distress and highest joy arise.

There is always the tendency in considering the needs of personality to try to fit behavior into an oversimplified scheme. The application of the four wishes of Thomas—for security, recognition, new experience and response—often falls into this error.[4] The approach outlined by Murray is, on the other hand, much more inclusive and scientific.[5] We shall not attempt to outline his theory of needs or reproduce here his list of twenty needs, but his work is worth careful study. Clergymen, because of the nature of some of their work, are likely to fall into the danger of oversimplification of personality needs and problems, and they should guard against this. Study of a technical work like Murray's is a good antidote for oversimplification.

FUNCTION AND STRUCTURE IN PERSONALITY

Every personality is constantly functioning toward certain ends. These ends may be clear or obscure, real or fantastic, social or antisocial, or subject to many other types of characterization, but they are the center of personality expression. A living person is always striving for something, and can be fully understood only in terms of this striving for values.

In striving for the satisfaction of needs, persons meet many conflicts and frustrations. This is true from birth to death, though the conflict and frustrations of childhood are the most significant for personality development. Frustration and conflict always involve the denial of a value, the failure to achieve the satisfaction of a need. It is not possible for any person to have all his needs satisfied all the time. But health requires a certain minimum of satisfaction in addition to the proper handling of the frustrations which are inevitable. With children, at least, the manner in which a frustration is imposed may be more significant than the frustration itself. Conflict and frustration occur in social experience and may involve any personality need.

Conflict and frustration always create a problem in the relationship of the personality to his world. The seriousness of this problem is not fully appreciated by most persons. However, personality integration and growth are seriously affected and personality development is determined largely by the age, intensity, and method used in meeting the conflict.

The fact that conflict and frustration are so much a result of cultural forces should not lead to a hastily drawn conclusion that culture is, therefore, evil and should be done away with. As a matter of fact, culture cannot be done away with; it can only be changed. Culture is the sum total of the ways in which man satisfies his needs in relation to other men. Only the psychotic can find satisfaction of his needs apart from others, and even he cannot do it completely or satisfactorily. Thus patterns of marriage and family life, patterns of economic, social, and religious life, are means through which human needs are satisfied and human values achieved. But cultural patterns become tools for the achievement of lesser ends, and then they become unhealthy. Thus family life may be used as a form through which one individual dominates a group, rather than for the mutual satisfactions of all concerned; economic patterns may be and are warped to serve the ends of financial gain rather than personality needs; religious patterns may be and are used to promote a dogma or support an entrenched authority rather than for the achievement of the larger values of religion. Our problem is not to dispose of culture; but rather to change cultural patterns and values so that unnecessary conflicts and frustrations are greatly lessened if not eliminated.

But so long as human personality requires other personalities for the satisfaction of its needs there will be a culture and there will also be conflict and frustrations. For many human impulses are destructive of group living, and human beings are fundamentally selfish. In the amazing capacity of personality to turn its destructive impulses into constructive achievement and to balance its selfishness with an equal amount of self-giving lies the hope for the salvation of humanity. For the task of achieving this transformation there is required a culture which not only seeks to reduce frustrations to a necessary minimum, but which learns to impose necessary frustrations in a spirit of fairness and justice, and which at every stage of development offers suitable compensations and substitute satisfactions. A culture like ours, in which it is largely a case of "every man for himself and the devil take the hindmost," will inevitably leave a great many of its members to the devil, in the form of physical, mental, and character illnesses.

It is not within the scope of this book to deal in detail with the various psychological conflicts found in personality, nor with the various psychological mechanisms utilized in resolving them. For material on these important topics the reader is referred to other works.[6]

Through its impact on the individuals, the culture becomes inextricably woven into the patterns of personality, largely in the development of attitudes and through the response of the individual to cultural pressures and influences. An individual may deal with his conflict, for example, by the process of projection and may believe that there is no problem within himself but only in other people. Repressing his own hatred of others, he believes that others are hating him and that they are against him or persecuting him. Such attitudes and ideas become dominant in his personality. They serve the function of easing his emotional tension. They also become structuralized in his personality. They become an habitual way of meeting life, or a form through which his personality finds more or less constant expression.

In a previous section the concepts of function and structure were discussed largely on the physical level. Through psychological structure the function of adaptation to the social and natural environment is carried out. Psychological function and structure cannot be separated; they are but two aspects of one living process. Unhealthy psychological mechanisms, such as projection and its resulting delusions, are not the cause of an illness; they are rather the structure through which a personality expresses a negative reaction to a life problem. Behind the use of such structure there is always the failure of the personality to make a more adequate adaptation or to achieve integration on a socially acceptable and personally satisfying level—the failure of a positive function. Whether the organism is functioning in the direction of integration or of disintegration, whether it is succumbing to the tensions of living or finding means of compensating for its frustrations, whether it is progressing through the various stages of growth or regressing to some earlier level—these and other functions all find expression in the psychological structure of the personality.

The psychological functions and structure of personality do not exist apart from the other structures of the organism. They are closely related to the chemical and physical functions and structures. Indeed, these should be thought of as different aspects of the life of the organism as a whole. The organism reacts to its experiences and carries out its functions, operating on all levels at the same time or, better, reacting and functioning as a whole. The chemical, physical, and psychological reactions are really three expressions of one reaction, and, in the words of Dr. White, "the same laws hold for the manifestations of reactions at the social, psychic and somatic levels."[7] Dr. Lewis states it more specifically: "To me the chemical reactions of the integrated tissues, the mechanics of the several physical tissue systems, and the psychological behavior of the individual in his relations to society are merely different aspects of the same thing; in short, are activities of the different levels of expression, and in disorders of the personality, whether such disorders are expressed mainly at the chemical, physical or psychological (electronic, cellular or symbolic) levels, a corresponding deviation must be present in the other aspects."[8]

These statements are based on intensive study of a large number of cases at St. Elizabeth's Hospital in Washington in which the material was classified in terms of the reaction type and the disease manifested. The 1,150 patients were divided into four groups: paranoid, schizoid, cycloid, and epileptoid. It was found that the incidence of death from tuberculosis was three times greater in the schizoid group than in the other three groups together. White interprets this in the following way: He points out that the schizoid patient shows little or no attempt to get well psychologically or to react to his problems in a compensatory way. He succumbs to the strain that produces the psychosis, and tends to deteriorate psychologically. There is a similar reaction on the physical level. "Such persons not only are easily infected, relatively speaking, but easily die of tuberculosis. They show no ability to protect themselves from its ravages. They neither get well nor develop a fibrosis, which results in a slowly progressing chronic type of infection. . . . A psychosis that is non-compensatory at the psychologic level occurs in a person of non-compensatory type at the somatic level. It is significant, too, that both types of reaction, the psychologic and the somatic, may be properly classified as regressive."[7]

On the other hand, the same study showed that death from circulatory disorders was most frequent in the paranoid group and cycloid groups and least frequent in the schizoid groups. Paranoid and cycloid groups react on the psychological level in a compensatory manner, that is, they defend themselves against tensions arising from some defect by overemphasizing some other aspect of their personalities. The paranoids do this through a delusional system; the cycloids more by over-activity. On the physical level, circulatory disorders are also of a compensatory nature. Thus White states that in these figures there is to be found an association between a mental illness that is compensatory and a physical illness that is also compensatory, as compared with the relatively low incidence of the same physical illness in the schizoid group which is non-compensatory in nature.

A similar picture is shown by the incidence of carcinoma and malignant tumor, which is three times greater for the paranoid and cycloid groups together than for the schizoid and epileptoid groups together. Says White: "The analogy here is fascinating as that between a delusional system which grows at the expense of the personality and a group of cells that grows at the expense of the body; or as Lewis puts it, 'Cancer is paranoia at the cellular level.' This association is to my mind sufficiently significant not only from the psychiatric point of view but also from the point of view of cellular pathology, so that even if carcinoma should ever be found to be associated with a micro-organism as an etiologic factor, the proliferative type of reaction would be just as significant." On the basis of these facts, White concludes "that the characteristics of the person at whatever level he is examined will be found reflected in all other levels, in other words, throughout the organism as a whole."

The relation between the structure of personality as it is revealed in personality types and tendencies toward specific physical illnesses is discussed in an article from a different source.[9] This study reports the results of a survey of 1,500 cases admitted to a large city hospital over a period of ten years, in approximately 80 per cent of which an important psychic factor was found to be operative. In regard to the personality make-up of patients, the author reports: "Even more interesting than the high percentage of patients in whom we found the emotional component in the illness important, however, were our observations concerning the types of persons that succumb to different types of illness. Of course we mean by this personality in terms of physical as well as psychological make-up. Patients in each of the disease groups studied showed fundamental similarities in the constellation, somatic make-up, major emotional conflicts, character resistances or characteristic ways of dealing with problems. They differed in these respects from patients in each other group studied although no factor was definitive." Studies of the patients admitted because of fractures and patients admitted because of coronary disease brought out, in the words of the author, the following personality differences: "First, both groups were in conflict with authority and in both cases the onset of illness coincided with circumstances which made this conflict acute.

"Second, these two groups of patients had completely different ways of dealing with authority; the former attempted to avoid any type of subjection to authority by becoming adventurers, by frequent changes of environment, occupation, boss and sometimes even wife; whereas the latter tended to stick to one job, usually their first job, for many years, working long hours without vacations until they themselves had become the authority. This tendency was borne out even by the history of marriage and divorce and size of family. Whereas about the same percentage of each group married, the average size of family for the coronary patients was much greater than that for the general population, whereas the average size of family in the fracture group fell far below the average for the general population. The educational charts indicate that this personality tendency toward self discipline and persistence among coronary patients and toward impulsive activity among fracture patients started early in life and was characteristic of the group in question: the fracture patients had a tendency to leave school in the middle of an educational unit, and the coronary patients only after they had completed an educational unit."

Studying the same group of patients in terms of their occupations, some interesting facts bearing on personality trends were discovered. For example, the great majority of the patients suffering from angina were found to fall in the occupational class, "proprietors, managers and officials." This was true also for coronary disease, although there was a large incidence of coronary disease in the "clerks, salesmen and stenographers" group. On the other hand, the largest group of fracture patients fell among the "clerks, salesmen and stenographers" and the second largest among "skilled workers." "Unskilled workers," in whom a high rate of accidents might be expected, showed even a lower incidence than "proprietors, managers and officials," who fell below the skilled workers.

These findings are interpreted in the light of Sherrington's statement that the most satisfactory release of instinctual tension is action, the least satisfactory is thought, and speech stands halfway between. "There is a great difference between the people who on receiving 'bad news' dash down to the ball field or to a movie, or to work, as compared with those who take time to go off by themselves and think it over, or those who call in the neighbors or make a round of visits to their friends to tell them what has happened. The physiological accompaniments of the emotion aroused seem to be different in each case. In our observation, constitutional and other factors being equal, the patient with coronary disease or hypertension inclines to keep his feelings to himself and think whereas the patient with the accident habit has a long history of impulsive action under stress."[9] The high incidence of angina and coronary disease among clerks, salesmen and stenographers in comparison with the low incidence among skilled and unskilled workers suggests personality factors in relation to these diseases. Certainly the skilled and unskilled workers have more opportunity to work out their tensions in activity, while they do not experience certain tensions peculiar to positions of great responsibility in which thought rather than action is the predominant outlet.

The relation of personality structure or type to various kinds of mental illness is commonly accepted in the mental hospital. Thus the schizophrenic illness is most likely to develop in a personality which has been shy, seclusive and withdrawing, tending to work out its tensions in fantasy rather than activity. The paranoid illness is most likely to develop in the person who has been seclusive, suspicious, bitter, and resentful and who has a strong tendency, before illness, to place blame on other people. The manic illness tends to develop in persons who are highly emotional in their responses; the depressed phase, in persons who are rigid and severe with themselves; the excited phase, in persons who tend to discharge their tensions in activity and in speech. These facts emphasize what we have already said, that mental illness represents the exaggeration of trends already present in the personality. It is for this reason that the study of the extremes in personality is so fruitful for an understanding of the so-called "normal" person.

Whether the symptoms of disease be manifest in the phys-ical, mental or character symptoms, disease is always an ex-perience of the whole personality. The classification of per-sonalities according to the labels "normal" and "abnormal" is frequently misleading and never instructive. It is a classifica-tion based on external criteria of what a personality should be like rather than on an understanding of the underlying functions which are being lived out. The major difference between the underlying processes of personality that make for disease and those which make for health is a difference of degree rather than one of kind. Given certain conditions, the stomach, for example, carries out its function of digestion through the usual processes, which involve the secretion of certain juices. Given other conditions, say a period of intense anxiety, the secretion of the juices may be inhibited or in-creased, thus interfering with the function of digestion. The laws of nature operate constantly and consistently. Given one set of conditions, they produce one result; given other conditions, they produce other results. The same is true on the psychological level; indeed, as we have seen, the same laws operate on all levels. Certain external and internal conditions produce an equilibrium in personality which we call health; other conditions produce a disequilibrium which we call illness. If our statistics have any meaning, it would appear that conditions producing disease are as common today as those producing health. Defining the normal in terms of cultural average, it may be more normal today to be sick than to be well. Viewed in terms of his internal psychological functions, the go-getter idealized in our culture may be really a sick man.

Disease is always the experience of a person. It is also the expression of basic processes within the personality. As we have seen, the reactions of the personality to various crises and tensions and the capacity of the individual to make satisfying adaptations to varying external situations are highly significant in the production of disease. Disease may be considered, therefore, as a form of language, which, if it is understood, becomes the key that unlocks the secret of a person's fundamental struggle for existence, his basic attitude toward life, his deepest purposes and goals. Disease may be a symbolic expression of the conflict between elemental forces within the personality or between the personality and the environment, the understanding and solution of which are of vital importance for the ultimate health of the individual.

Personality factors have another relation to the disease process. They present a complicating factor, apart from the disease itself, and may thus throw the balance in the struggle for a satisfying adjustment. Disease, being experienced as a threat to the life of the organism, may mobilize other factors within the life of the individual which are threats to his security. There are present in every personality primitive tendencies, which never have been fully integrated or have not found their proper place in the development of character, and these may become the ally of disease, and complicate its course. There are also present in many persons external situations which create severe tension and from which an illness is a welcome release, temporary or otherwise. Such factors, internal or external, negatively influence recovery and are responsible for the chronic nature of much illness. Every physician is familiar with the patient who gives up the fight and makes no effort to get well. In a mental hospital one sometimes sees patients in whom an organic illness, such as tuberculosis, releases strong feelings of rebellion and resentment which have been smoldering within the person for years, and which in turn make successful treatment practically impossible. Similar patients are to be found in the general hospital, but with some variations.

Disease may have still another relation to the personality. It may bring profound changes in the personality. This is of course related to the tendency of disease to mobilize negative forces, but has an additional factor. Many of our social adjustments are built up on the basis of repression. Elements within the personality which may cause friction or hinder social adjustments are repressed. This repression requires the use of more or less energy, depending on the strength of the impulses repressed. Now, disease reduces the energy available to the organism both for ordinary life functions and for the function of repression of undesirable tendencies. Not having sufficient energy at its disposal, the personality is powerless against these undesirable tendencies, and they find expression either openly or in a disguised form. This is true not only of diseases that attack the physical functions but also of those which are primarily emotional. At such times individuals may undergo personality changes in various degrees. Thus physical illness may be accompanied by increased irritability, depression, or even undue elation in persons who do not usually show these trends. Delirium is an example of temporary personality disturbance under the stress of physical illness which greatly depletes energy and releases repressions. Many mental illnesses begin with gradual personality changes, the significance of which is usually discounted by family and friends until they develop into obvious problems.

The functions of the total personality are organized and expressed through various structures. A breakdown in structure is indicative of a breakdown in function. Behind the breakdown in function there lies a problem in the experience of the individual, and a reaction that has rendered him incapable of proper functioning. Ultimately the problems of illness and health rest on the experience of the individual, and are the outgrowth of his particular way of life.

RELIGION AND HEALTH

The life of the organism finds expression on various levels, which may be studied as separate systems but are never fully understood apart from their relation to the whole. Personality is the manifestation of the life of the whole organism. The mind is the organ that serves the function of integration of the whole personality. In this function the mind deals with both the facts of existence and the meaning of existence with the aid of symbols. Meaning or value is the center around which personality becomes organized. The failure to achieve meaning of a positive nature results in a failure in the integration of personality, and leads to illness.

Religion represents man's struggle with the facts of existence in an endeavor to find the underlying relationships that give them meaning, and to create a way of life based on his resulting insight into the nature and meaning of life. To the extent that religion has succeeded in this task it has provided a basis for the integration of personality and of the social group, and has been a strong force for personal and social health. To the extent that it has failed it has become, in one way or another, a force leading to illness. Basically religion is not an illusion; it is man's attempt to find that reality which is capable of sustaining personality through the inescapable tragedies of life. Religion becomes illusion only when it fails in its proper function and the mind becomes ill.

The discovery that disease is the result of a life process in which both individual and environmental factors play important roles raises the problem of the relationship between religion and health, for religion serves an important function in personality-environment relationships. The discovery of the emotional component in disease process, in both its causative and its curative aspects, raises the question of the place of religion in the emotional life of man. One evidence of this is the fact that psychoanalysis, developing primarily as a technique of mental healing, has not been able to carry on its work and avoid the study of religion. [10] "One of the most striking results of modern developments of our knowledge concerning the influence of mental factors in disease," says Dr. W. H. R. Rivers, "is that they are bringing back medicine in some measure to that cooperation with religion which existed in the early stages of human progress." [11]

Against this background, we shall consider, in the next section, the relation of religion to one of man's most perplexing problems, the tendency to become ill.

REFERENCES

1. For excellent discussions of the problem of personality see ALLPORT, GORDON W., *Personality, A Psychological Interpretation* (New York, 1937) and ÁNGYAL, ANDRAS, *Foundations for a Science of Personality* (New York, 1941).
2. HALDANE, J. S., *Respiration,* p. 125. New Haven, 1922.
3. WILDE, OSCAR, *The Ballad of Reading Gaol.*
4. THOMAS, W. I., *The Unadjusted Girl.* New York, 1923.
5. MURRAY, HENRY A., *et al., Explorations in Personality.* New York, 1938.
6. BROWN, J. F., *The Psychodynamics of Abnormal Psychology* (New York, 1940); HORNEY, K., *Neurotic Personality of Our Time* (New York, 1938); MENNINGER, K., *The Human Mind* (New York, 1937).

7. WHITE, W. A., "The social significance of mental disease," *Archives of Neurology & Psychiatry*, 22: 1929, pp. 873-900.
8. LEWIS, N. D. C., "A discussion of the relationship of the chemical, physical and psychological aspects of personality," *Psychoanalytic Review*, 11: 1924, pp. 403-414.
9. DUNBAR, FLANDERS, "Emotions and bodily changes," *Annals of Internal Medicine*, 14: 1940, p. 839.
10. REIK, T., "The therapy of the neuroses and religion," *International Journal of Psychoanalysis*, 10: 1929, pp. 292-302.
11. RIVERS, W. H. R., *Medicine, Magic and Religion*, p. 144. New York, 1924.

SECTION TWO

RELIGION IN ILLNESS AND HEALTH

CHAPTER VI

EXPERIENCE AND SYMBOLS IN RELIGION

THE EXPERIENCE OF MARY JONES

THE illness which brought Mary Jones, a young woman of twenty-two, to the hospital was expressed largely in religious forms. Several weeks before admission she began to read *Pilgrim's Progress* very intently. She spoke of herself as Pilgrim and thought she was going through the same experience as Bunyan ascribed to Pilgrim. A few days later she became excited and talked a great deal on religious subjects. She spoke of herself as a "disciple," and felt that she was called to give her life to religious work. She further believed that a certain young man also was called by God to devote his life with her to religious work. She then sent an application for admission to a Bible school. She stated that she had been crucified, and would stand against the wall with her arms outstretched. Then she came to believe that her physical body was gone, that only the spirit remained. Frequently she would be heard to say, "Oh, Lord, show me the light. There is no such thing as darkness on earth, no hell. The world will not be saved by Christ. The sun will be darkened, the night will turn into day."

This illness was the culmination of a conflict that had been raging in her mind for two years. An operation had been performed at that time to relieve severe pain which had accompanied her menstrual periods since their onset at the age of twelve. This operation made her very conscious of her sexual organs and desires. She had never been instructed along sexual lines, and her attitudes toward sex were such as to create a strong sense of guilt in her mind.

Outwardly she became nervous, melancholy, and irritable, and spent a great deal of time alone in her room.

Her conflict was intensified by another experience. She fell in love with a young man whom she idealized. Her illusions were rudely shattered by his attempt to persuade her to engage in petting parties. Petting represented to her a kind of love that was dark and sinister; her idea of love was highly idealistic.

In her diary she wrote about this conflict. Her ability to articulate her feelings affords insight into her struggles. She frankly confessed a strong physical desire, but also repudiated this as sinful. She affirmed her belief in a kind of love that is "spiritual." Writing of her struggle, she says: "The spiritual and the sensual in a sensitive passionate nature combat in constant warfare. A strong ardent passion, suddenly aroused, becomes like a fiery demon, the desire of the flesh and body arises; the soul in a predominating spiritual nature aspires to high goals and the combat between soul and body begins."

She endeavors to find a solution for her problem in religion as she understands it. "Love! Was this love? O God! teach me to understand," she sighed heavily, bounding from her bed, tears coursing down her cheeks as she knelt at the bedside to commune with that Immortal Being who she knew would come to her rescue. She could talk to her "Heavenly Father," for "God" knew all things. "He" who numbered the hairs of one's head knew of the dull aching burden in one's heart. Had not "He" taught her to realize that she could not idolize a human being as she had idolized C., that boys were only boys after all, and could not be depended on at all times and now that affair was over. She had thought she was free of burdens. Free, only to fall into a larger pitfall; a deeper darkness, for it was dark. The future loomed like a fathomless pool of mire, black and sinister, far into space and she was afraid of it, afraid of life, of love, if this was "love."

"Dear, dear God," she entreated in passionate ejaculation.

"Please, dear God, help me." Should love be like this? Should love be black and sinister? Love is light, love is beautiful. It should light our way. "O God, please help me to love that way. Help me to make love beautiful, to understand it. Do I really love him?" and she clutched at her heart in an apprehensive gesture. Is it love to desire him, his nearness, his love more than anything in all the world? "Oh!" she cried, "I want him to love me. I do love him. Why, it must be love when I'd leave all I have if he'd love me honorably, if he'd be my friend first, I could teach him to love me honorably."

While burdened with this conflict, she became ill and spent some time in bed. Of this period she wrote: "For several weeks the days succeeded in a dreamy haze; unconscious of the outer world she lived in a world of her own; having built a stronger faith in the imaginary, she continued in her daily task of duty as one in a dream. The hours of the night stretched through a panorama of romantic adventure. Of cool, sparkling frothy waves licking the sands; of a fair eyed youth strolling by her side on a long stretch of sandy beach along the water's edge; the touch of a large rough hand which sent her blood tingling; the tender persuasive smile which held her embraced and the strong magnetic personality which drew her into this world of dreams grew stronger as time wore on.

"Her scope of visions widened in countless scenes of romantic splendor; gliding over the smooth surface of a shimmering lake; twinkling stars overhead and the soft yellow glow of a full moon upon the golden ripples above a lowering forehead; countless whispered caresses and ever that strong magnetic force drawing her into an unfathomable depth which she fought frantically to comprehend."

She has some insight into the effect of this conflict on her health, for she writes: "It is not well for the mind to probe too deep within the immaterial, nor to dwell too long upon past reflections nor to contrive ways and means for the imaginary future, for a continual turmoil or mind controversy weakens physical powers and the victim of such, being physically weak and mentally shaken, contracts physical disease readily."

She brooded over her experiences, seeking an answer. "Yesterday's adventure had raised havoc with the consoling resolutions; the doubt that her desired lover would not meet her standards of love sent her thoughts madly over events. She recalled every incident, every word and expression of her romantic adventure over and over, trying to detect the demeanor of her admired escort.

Her diary contains many prayers to God for help in this struggle. Typical of these prayers is the following: "Oh, dear Father in Heaven, please hear my prayer," and she burst forth in a passionate outburst of weeping. "Why does it hurt so?" "Why should I love him like this? I haven't the privilege," she stated emphatically. "Why do I feel it is wrong to love this way? Why do I doubt him? Why can't I believe him? The world calls it love when we'd leave everyone and everything we possess for the love of one in honor.

"Please, God, give me strength to use discretion, to do right. Dear God, understand someone must help me. Thou dost understand Thy people for Thou art our Maker. Please, as in Bible times, please help us today in our weaknesses, in our trials and temptations.

"O God, make him do right and teach me a good clean unselfish love, teach me to understand why I love him so, why I'd leave all my relatives, all those who are so near to me. Yes, I'd leave every one of them for him."

Eventually another feeling is expressed in her writing. It is hate; hate toward this boy who has caused her so much agony. Several times she writes, speaking to the boy friend: "Go ahead and make love to me so I can hate you. I'd hate you if you pretended to love me and I wish to God that I could." Her voice trembled with emotion. "No, I won't," he replied with emphasis. "I don't want you to hate me. I don't want to pull you down. I admire you and I want you to feel the way you do about me."

Again: "Loving him one minute, hating him the next, emitting a wry grimace at the thought, clenching knuckles firmly upon the iron bar and swallowing hard to choke down the hard, dry sobs which arose from time to time; hating herself for her weakness, hating the world in general, and asking herself why, oh, why, must she bear such agony."

Gradually more and more of despair creeps into her diary. She wants to leave home, to go far away. She writes her epitaph: "Here lies Miss ——. Died of a broken heart. Life was too hard to bear. Love too great a test. Died a coward."

And as if trying to sum up her problems: "Could youth but fathom the labyrinth of life; the blindness of youthful passions; the idleness of romance and the depth of Immortal Love, there would be no lessons to learn on that journey to mature life when the curtain is drawn from the past and the fruits of youthful labor come into view; when the seed is sown and time for harvest is ripe. Youth is free, unencumbered with knowledge, uncomprehending the dangers of unbridled passions; following blindly in labyrinthian ways; guided only by the instinct of natural forces and the immortal hand of Providence."

She was unable to find her way out of the labyrinth and to achieve a healthy way of life. Instead, she withdrew more and more from reality and sought a solution in the world of unreality, which found expression in religious forms.

This was not the first occasion in which she had struggled with hard reality. The death of her mother when she was six years of age puzzled her very much. She wondered why her mother had been taken away and why she could not be with her mother. She dreamed about her mother and of being up in the sky. Since she did not have a mother to confide in, she kept her troubles to herself. She considered that she was too deep in life and that her father never understood her.

During adolescence, Mary is described as being very sensitive and inclined to accept blame easily. She took the cares of the world on her own shoulders, and tried to conceal her own problems from herself. She was always concerned with what others thought of her, and tried not to offend others. She was shy and retiring, though at times succeeded in asserting herself. She was usually serious, and did not have a sense of humor. In all her thinking she was idealistic, particularly in choosing friends and in her ideas about love. She spent a great deal of time with an aunt who read the Bible and talked religion to her. She was never active in church, nor did she attend services regularly. The inner struggle which ended in illness was carried on without any attempt to get aid from others or from the church.

RELIGIOUS SYMBOLS AND THE REALITIES OF EXPERIENCE

At the outset it is important to remember that we do not have a complete history of this patient, and that there are probably many factors in her illness of which we know nothing. But what we do know about her enables us to arrive at some understanding of the significance of religion in her life and in her illness. The first step toward this understanding is the recognition that her religious speech and actions were forms or symbols through which her life problem was crystallized and expressed. This problem involved her whole personality, though it had physical, psychological, and social components. The meaning of the life processes working out within her found expression in her religious symbols.

Many superficial observers would point out that the mentally ill use the religious symbols as do individuals who are not ill, but without a meaning. However, experienced workers seem to agree that even the most bizarre set of symbols has a meaning. The meaning may be concealed from both patient and observer, and may be difficult or impossible to determine. Later, we shall discuss more fully the tendency of unhealthy minds to use religious symbols as a means of concealment. Here we are concerned only with the principle that, as in this patient, religious symbols are the means through which realities within the experience of the person may find expression, whether these be constructive or destructive in their outcome. In her life history we get some insight into the nature of some of these realities.

With the death of her mother at the age of six, we see first a reaction of bewilderment and questioning. She wondered why she could not be with her mother and why the mother had been taken away. Life had presented her with a difficult problem. Apparently she received little or no effective aid from others in her environment. Already there was developing a tendency to meet frustrations by building up an ideal world in fantasy, and to seek the answer to her questions in her own inner world. She seemed to live in the sky, and considered herself to be "too deep in life" and that others were not deep enough to understand her. This is a typical reaction of a child who is much involved in her own fantasies—others cannot share them. The religious teachings received from her aunt were used by her to reinforce this idealizing tendency.

The tendency to idealize one's world is found normally in childhood, and is a natural concomitant of the helplessness and inadequacy of the child. It may be overdeveloped through a series of frustrating experiences not directly connected with religion. On the other hand, and this seems to be true of this patient, religious teaching, especially in childhood and adolescence, may serve to crystallize and to reinforce this tendency to an extent that results in unhealthy withdrawal from real situations. We emphasize this fact, not to defend religion, but to indicate something of the relation of religious teaching and beliefs to tendencies already present within the personality. Failure to understand that religious teaching may not so much create something new in the personality as to mobilize and give expression to something already there leads at times to ineffectiveness and at other times to actual support of unhealthy tendencies. This problem needs much more attention than does the logical nature of religious teaching, and requires a real skill in understanding personality trends.

We do not have a very complete picture of the experience of this girl through later childhood and adolescence. The description of her personality trends is significant. She was sensitive and inclined to accept blame easily. These tendencies are exaggerated in her mental illness. The tendency to accept blame easily contains as many dangers for the personality as does the tendency to shift all the blame on to others and to refuse to accept it on a real basis. More than this, she took the cares of the world on her own shoulders, as though to increase her suffering. She also tried to conceal her own problems to herself, in other words, to avoid them and repress her true feelings. Concern with the cares of the world was a means of avoiding her own problems, and a substitute expression for her anxiety. She was shy and retiring, a defensive reaction against a world that was too much for her, and a reaction which utilized her tendency to live in fantasy. These personality traits are indicative of a person who has suffered severely from life. The fact that occasionally she showed a degree of self-assertiveness is amplified in her diary. Actually, her suppressed feelings would increase to the point where some minor situation would release the control, and she would explode violently. These explosions were followed by periods of remorse for her behavior.

It is with this personality background that she encountered a severe crisis at the age of twenty. This crisis, which arose on the physical and social levels, created a profound psychological conflict, and presented a problem for her whole personality. The writings in her diary illustrate the principle that religious symbols are used to express realities central in the experience of the personality and to search for a solution to the problem of the personality.

We shall pass over the possible psychological significance of her menstrual difficulties, as this is not clear. It is clear that the operation brought an unusually strong reaction in terms of a new consciousness of sex for which she was totally unprepared emotionally. This new consciousness was accompanied by a strong feeling of guilt. She was suddenly faced with impulses which up to this time she had successfully repressed from consciousness. The operation had the psychological effect of weakening her powers of repression, and she was faced with impulses she did not dare to express, but which threatened to overpower her.

While in the midst of this conflict she fell in love with a young man. She attempted to live out this experience on the basis of a highly idealized view of love, quite out of harmony with the point of view of her boy friend. The ensuing conflict is apparent from her writings as given above. It was a conflict between the idealized world in which she had been living and the real world in which she was trying to live.

At this point the real significance of her idealized view of love may be made clear. Her idea is not that of a healthy young woman of twenty-two, but is rather more in harmony with a small child's view of love, a relationship of dependence, protection, and receiving from the lover. She was looking for someone to take the role of a father rather than that of a lover. She had a strong need for affection of this kind, but was incapable of the kind that would lead to a happy marriage. Her personality had not matured at this point; it had remained childish. She was, therefore, unable to deal with a situation arising on an adult level. She experienced deep guilt and anxiety, and sought a solution through religion. Gradually her frustrated love gave way to hate, and she hated the boy friend, herself, and her world. This hate only increased her guilt, and became an important factor in her gradual breakdown. When the conflict was at its highest, a strong social support was removed by the death of her aunt. Gradually her personality disintegrated, as she withdrew more and more from the real world and her impulses found expression in fantastic and bizarre ideas and behavior.

The precipitating factor in this girl's illness was the conflict over sex. The basic underlying factor was that she had failed to mature emotionally in a healthy manner. A personality with emotional maturity equal to her years would have been able to handle this conflict; indeed, such a personality probably would not have had this conflict. Her view of sex and her use of religion are reflections of her failure to grow. Deep in her personality was the tendency to withdraw from harsh reality and live in the make-believe world, which is so characteristic of childhood. This tendency is also expressed in her religion, and this will be discussed more fully later. The sex conflict was too much for her unstable, immature personality, and an illness was the only solution she could find.

In her illness, as in the period of intense conflict, she found expression for impulses, reactions, ideas, and values in religious symbols. As the illness began, she identified herself with Pilgrim and thought she was going through the same experience. Pilgrim was undoubtedly the symbolic expression of Bunyan's experience of conflict and illness, which had some features similar to her own. The call to religious work is a frequent idea in persons at the early stages of this kind of mental illness, though it should be added that is not always symptomatic of such an illness. The truth or fallacy of an idea rests on objective criteria, and not on the psychological mechanism by which it happens to be employed in a given personality. The belief that she had been crucified is her way of expressing the idea of death, which also is common in such illnesses, and contains an element of identification with Christ as well as the idea of punishment for sin. The belief that her physical body was gone and that only her spirit remained is the final expression of her idealization of love, which denied its physical aspects. Her prayer for light is a repetition of a universal need and experience, for light is essential to the solution of any problem and light is a common human quest. [1] But she was unable to find the light for which she prayed, and her personality became ill under the stress of an intense and unsolved problem.

Summarizing, this patient found herself faced, on the one hand, with powerful instinctive urges of a childish nature which threatened to get out of her weak control and, on the other hand, with a severe conscience which sought the renunciation of these urges. A combination of physical, psychological, and social experiences created a problem for her personality as a whole. The intense mental suffering which she experienced is indicative of the seriousness of her inner disorder. In the terms of the first section, there was a complete lack of integration on both psychological and social levels and also on the physical level. The problem of individuation also is clear. She could not adequately direct the various elements of her personality into their rightful place; indeed, she could not accept herself as she was, much less adequately express herself in satisfying activities. Socially, she could not take her place with others as an independent personality, but was in danger either of being submerged by the group or of withdrawing from the group. She did the latter in order to avoid the former. She could not maintain her individuality and still be one of the group. The fundamental problem of this girl was similar to that of every human being—the adjustment of her life to an environment, both internal and external, which gave her many painful conflicts and frustrations.

This conflict, though perhaps not the sole cause of her psychosis, is nevertheless one of the major causes. It is also the central problem in her religious experience and ideas. Religious symbols offered her the form into which she poured the dynamic, fluid experience of her inner life and through which this experience eventually crystallized as it developed into processes which produced illness. An experience in which there was a decreasingly satisfactory relationship with the objective world and an increasing tendency to withdraw into herself would inevitably produce a subjective kind of religion, the symbolic structure of which would reflect this subjectivity. Her diary might well be called *Pilgrim's Regress*.

It should not be inferred from this chapter that the truth of an idea rests on the psychological mechanism that controls its use in a given personality. Obviously, truth or fallacy must rest on objective criteria, such as value. But an understanding of the psychological mechanism by which a given idea is used does reveal the function of that idea in a given personality. The best possible idea may be warped by some persons for pathological purposes. This is of great importance, for religion has tended to overemphasize the former to the neglect of the latter and has therefore found itself faced with seemingly insuperable problems in dealing with personality. A balance is much to be desired. Theology and the psychology of religion cannot neglect each other without becoming one-sided. In the following chapters we shall deal primarily with the psychological processes involved in the use of religious symbols and ideas in successful and unsuccessful solution of life problems. But in doing this we do not mean to imply that the testing of religious ideas in a philosophical manner should be neglected.

REFERENCES

1. An interesting interpretation of the biological origins of religion in terms of the quest for light is to be found in Oliver L. Reiser, "The biological origins of religion," *Psychoanalytic Review*, 19: 1932, pp. 1-22. Sun and light symbolism is prominent in both Hebrew and Christian religions.

CHAPTER VII

THE FUNCTION AND STRUCTURE OF RELIGION

RELIGION AND ORGANISM-ENVIRONMENT RELATIONSHIPS

IN THE preceding chapter the use of religious symbols to express realities within the experience of the individual was discussed. In this chapter we shall deal with the function of integration and growth of personality, and the way in which this is carried out through religious symbols.

In all our previous discussions we have stressed the close and dynamic relationship which exists between the organism or the personality and the environment. The environment may influence the structural development of the personality on the chemical, physiological, or psychological level. The organism responds to environmental influences on the basis of inherent laws and functions, and it may act on the environment before it reacts to the environment. The relation of the living organism to its environment is so close that there is a sense in which it is true that the organism and the environment are one.

The relation of the personality to its world is extremely important for health and equally so for religion. This world, or total environment, is both an external world and an inner world. The life of the individual takes place as it were between these two worlds; the conscious ego faces two ways and has the task of reconciling conflicting pressures. To be a self-conscious, functioning person involves the power to distinguish at least to a measure "I" and "other-than-I." To be an integrated, growing person requires a kind of relationship which, at least to a degree, organizes one's inner world and one's external world into an harmonious whole. This relationship forms the basis of the reaction of the individual to his world and grows out of his interpretation of the meaning of his experience with that world. The reaction pattern will differ according to whether the individual feels that his relationship is yielding security and satisfaction or threats and frustration. Successful integration and growth will be much more difficult or even impossible in a relationship that yields fear and insecurity than in one which creates security.

Now, the ability to apprehend and formulate this relationship in terms of ideas and to express it conceptually is unique in man. This apprehension of relationships is an important function of personality and provides the basis for integration on the higher psychological and social levels. In other words, any animal, say a dog, is capable of reflex action and of a certain integration of reflex activity. But it cannot experience integration in terms of conscious purpose, which requires insight into relationships through which integration is achieved.

The conceptualized relationship between an individual and his world is frequently spoken of as the philosophy of life. This term usually carries a connotation that is primarily intellectual. A person's relationship with his world is not primarily intellectual; it involves the emotional and the conative aspects of personality as well. Indeed, it is pretty well agreed that these are even more fundamental than the intellectual, though for the purposes of health each must be given its proper place. The word "Weltanschauung," for which there is no equivalent English word, signifies the conceptually formulated relationships of the individual and his world, in terms of feeling, intellect, and will, or his attitude toward the universe. Isolated acts or beliefs of an individual taken by themselves may be meaningless, but seen as the expression of the Weltanschauung they become intelligible. This is true in both illness and health, and in religion, except that in some forms of mental illness the Weltanschauung is much disturbed or seriously deteriorated. Here we see activity in which the part controls the whole.

In the previous section the fact that the organism reacts as a whole to its environment was discussed. Here we may say that the Weltanschauung is the subjective aspect of this total reaction; it is the organism's apprehension of this reaction in psychological terms or symbols. It is, therefore, not a mystical something, but a living reality that finds expression in the way of life and in specific activity.

In the formation of the Weltanschauung, experiences on all levels of life play a part. Chemical, physical, psychological, and cultural factors all contribute, in one way or another, to the total result. The psychoanalysts have made a valuable contribution in showing how experiences in the early days of childhood contribute to the attitude toward the universe held by the adult. They have made a unique contribution in showing how elements of experience below the level of consciousness play a varying but highly important role in total reaction of the organism. Weltanschauung is the apprehension of both inner and external worlds in terms of their significance to the personality as a whole, and of the endeavor of the person to deal with them.

Weltanschauung is the expression of the individual's relationship with his world. As such, it grows out of his experience. On the other hand, it creates the basis for further experiences. A child that has experienced relationships with people in authority in terms of fear will find itself regarding all authorities in similar terms. This attitude may not be well formulated, but it will be effective. Once an attitude is formulated, it tends to control the individual's interpretation of experience. Weltanschauung is not only determined by experience; in turn, it becomes a powerful determinant of experience. It directs the selection of situations to be experienced and those to be avoided, and governs the interpretation of all aspects of experience. Its primary function is to serve as a basis for the integration of personality, though many persons do not achieve the kind of Weltanschauung that makes integration possible.

When the individual becomes aware of the distinction between himself and his world, the formulation of Weltanschauung becomes implicit. If this relationship were such that no tensions were created, the Weltanschauung would probably remain in an undeveloped state. The fact is that tension-producing conflicts and frustrations arise early in every life, and some kind of solution is required. Conflict, frustration, and the necessity for a tension-reducing adjustment become the stimuli under which Weltanschauung is developed.

Becoming aware of a distinction between oneself and one's environment raises the question of personal identity. "Who am I?" and "What am I?" require an answer. They involve the relationship of the individual to his world. Conflict and frustration intensify these questions and raise others, particularly "Why?" Frequently the child asks "Why?" not out of curiosity, but in protest against a frustrating world. Adults do the same, though perhaps in a more sophisticated manner. It will be recalled that such questions are both implicit and expressed in the experience of the young woman whose case has been cited. "Must love be like this? Why does it hurt so?" she asks, as she thinks of life as a labyrinth to be fathomed. Such questions express the basic need for orientation to life as a whole and to its various components. They express the search for an answer that will ease the conflict and give a basis for inner peace and external adaptation, a search that failed in this girl's experience. Conflict and frustration thus stimulate the development of the Weltanschauung, but the factors determining whether that Weltanschauung is to be healthy or unhealthy are to be found in other aspects of the personality and also in the influence of the culture.

Evidence shows that the relationship of the organism and its environment is so close that in a sense the organism is one with its environment. It has also been shown that the organism reacts as a whole and that the same kind of reaction is to be found on each level of a given organism. This reaction is perceived by the individual in terms of an attitude toward the universe, a Weltanschauung. To the ex-

tent that Weltanschauung is consciously perceived and formulated the individual is conscious of what he is doing and
why. Since it is the expression of the organism as a whole, the
Weltanschauung has the highly significant capacity and function of controlling the behavior of the parts of the organism.
This is the function of integration. Through his attitude
toward his universe the individual seeks a basis on which
growth can take place, and through which he can find his
proper relation to other organisms like himself. It always
involves realities beyond the individual. In other words,
Weltanschauung serves the functions of integration and of
individuation.

Reviewing the material of the first section, the importance
of Weltanschauung for physical and mental illness becomes
clear. With the increasing insight into the emotional and environmental factors in disease comes the appreciation that
the patient's total outlook on life is highly significant. It is
at this point that the fundamental relationship between
religion and health arises. For religion provides its adherents
with a definite Weltanschauung, out of which a way of life,
or reaction pattern, develops. As we shall see, this Weltanschauung and its resulting way of life may be of a character
that leads to illness or to health. The reaction pattern of
the organism as a whole is highly significant in illness and
health. Religion is primarily concerned with this pattern.

In Chapter V we dealt with the question of the needs of
the personality and the experience of values. The Weltanschauung, being the expression of the fundamental attitudes
and relationships, includes the expression of man's world
of values. Man's fundamental questions about life are of two
kinds: questions of fact and questions of value. The Weltanschauung expresses his insight into questions of value
and determines the use he makes of his knowledge on questions of fact. For this reason a purely scientific Weltanschauung will never adequately meet the needs of human
life.

Now, religion brings to the individual a definite Weltanschauung. The word "religion," etymologically, means a binding together. Religion offers man a Weltanschauung that aims at binding together the diverse elements of the personality into an integrated whole, and at relating this whole in an harmonious way to the larger universe. "Wilt thou be made whole?" and "Thy will be done" are expressions of this central function.

It will be recognized that we are discussing religion in general. The actual Weltanschauung offered by various religions differs. Within organized Christianity there is also a difference, so that the Roman Catholic, and the Fundamentalist and Liberal in the Protestant Church differ. Yet each seeks to develop, in its respective group, a Weltanschauung through an answer to man's fundamental problems of the meaning and value of life, and on the basis of this to formulate a way of life which man ought to follow. The same inner tensions that may lead to illness are also a fundamental problem for religion, for salvation involves their solution.

Thus far in this book, and because most of our discussion has dealt with illness, we have emphasized the destructive nature of conflict and frustration. On the other hand, religion—or, to be more specific, the religion of Jesus—emphasizes the creative possibility of human personality. The insight that conflict and suffering may be dealt with creatively is an essential element in the Christian Weltanschauung that is in need of strong emphasis today on both individual and social levels. This insight is closely akin to that of the modern biologist, that the organism is equipped with powers of initiative and spontaneity, and hence does not react to its environment in a purely mechanical way. It is the fact that personality may deal creatively with conflict, that is, it may solve conflict in a way that yields values or creates satisfying relationships, that makes possible the higher development of personality. This same fact stimulates and reinforces the will to live and the will to get well.

Disease finds a fruitful field in the personality in which

the will to live and the will to get well have been weakened by the failure to find a creative solution for conflict and frustration. In actual illness the will not to get well or the desire to die may be more potent than any medicine. In terms of general personality development, there is a great difference between an adjustment in which the immediate reduction of specific tensions is the dominant aim and one in which the dominant aim is the creation of a more satisfying way of life. The first is easy, and frequently results in regressive behavior; the latter is more difficult. It involves an understanding of the internal and external causes of tensions, removing these causes where this is possible, learning how to accept them, to neutralize them harmlessly, or to turn them to constructive use when removal is not possible. This involves the capacity to make intelligent changes both in personality and in culture. An individual, under the pressure of inner tension, is likely to lose sight of the creative possibilities in his experience. On the other hand, religious teachers may overemphasize the creative possibilities of personality as a vague generality, without relating it sufficiently to the realities of experience. There is also a danger in emphasizing the possibility of a creative solution of conflict without offering adequate practical help.

The insight into the creative possibility of personality is related to the concept of the whole organism controlling the activity of its parts as a necessity for health. The creative solution of a conflict is always in terms of the whole personality. Thus the creative solution of a sex conflict cannot be made in terms of sex only, but in terms of the person as a whole. Dealing with sex on the basis of repression violates this basic principle, as it involves the control of one part of the personality by another part, the conscience, rather than the organization of each under a pattern that serves the best interests of the personality as a whole. Dealing with sex on the basis of unbridled expression violates the same principle from the other side. And since sex has its social as well as personal aspects, both physically and emotionally, the individual's relationship to his larger world, particularly other people, must be taken into consideration in any creative solution. Sex, physically and psychologically, is an important factor in personal and social integration, through its functions of attaining union with another person and of creative production of a new life. Any handling of sex that does not lead to such integration produces misery sooner or later, notwithstanding any immediate pleasurable gain.

The creative solution of conflict is not to be defined in terms of adherence to accepted cultural or moral patterns. Many persons who struggle valiantly to do the right thing, as defined either by their conscience or by cultural standards, find themselves in severe conflict and experience a gradual diminishing of those values which make life worth living. Persons who are very good in a conventional sense may find their goodness making them ill. Such persons also frequently make the lives of others unhappy. On the other hand, open disregard of cultural and moral patterns is not the valid criterion of inner health and maturity that it is sometimes held to be. The creative solution of conflict is rather a matter of inner adjustment and organization of urges, feelings, and ideas, a reorientation of the whole person toward goals or values that promote integration and growth.

The creative solution of any conflict involves a higher synthesis of the conflicting tendencies that makes possible their expression in ways producing values. Such synthesis is possible only when the Weltanschauung is sufficiently strong to enable the personality to gain mastery over its parts. Conflict is an indication of a weakness in integration and a need for growth. As such it is an opportunity as well as a hazard. Religion becomes creative when it provides men with a basis for new integrations resulting in personality development and more satisfying social relationships. One does not find in Jesus any suggestion that the higher values of life come through wishing. To him they come rather as the result of the creative synthesis of conflicting elements of experience, and such synthesis is not easily achieved, as his experience in the wilderness indicates.

THE SYMBOLIC STRUCTURE OF RELIGION

The central function of religion is to develop a Weltanschauung that will lead to integration and growth. Like all intangible functions, this must be expressed in more concrete forms. Religious symbols are the forms through which the basic religious attitude is structuralized and elaborated. Just as the brain and nervous system serve the function of integration on the physiological level, so religious symbols, properly organized and structuralized, serve the function of integration on the level of meaning and value.

A symbol is something that stands for something else. A vital religious symbol is a form through which a meaningful experience is expressed. In their highest development, religious symbols are forms through which a Weltanschauung is expressed, or to be more exact, the Weltanschauung of religion. Through living religious symbols the answers to man's fundamental questions in regard to the meaning of life are formulated, and a way of life is organized.

Symbols are of various kinds. An act, an object, a color, a sound may be symbols. Thus a kiss, a tree, the ringing of a bell may be symbols, and may express different meanings to different persons and at different times. When these are used as religious symbols they become an outward and sensuous form through which an inner and spiritual reality is apprehended and expressed.

Speech, the spoken and written word, is the highest form of symbolic expression of which man is capable. The ability to formulate the meaning of experience through word symbols distinguishes man from all other animals. Indeed, consciousness itself, which is capable of a much higher degree of development in man than in other animals, is developed largely through speech symbols. When an experience is verbalized it is raised from the level of unawareness to that of consciousness. Thought itself may not always be on the level of consciousness, but it cannot be consciously formulated without words. Through words man captures and gives a more or less permanent structure to fleeting experiences and meanings. Through word symbols man is able to apprehend, interpret, and organize his total relationships. Such organization not only crystallizes the past; it is a major factor in determining the future direction of personality. The function of consciousness is that of integration and direction.

On the physical level meaning may be expressed by an act; on the psychological level, through word symbols. Word symbols, being tools for the development of consciousness, are tools for the expression and development of Weltanschauung. The group mind has expressed its insight into the close relation between word symbols and inner reality in the proverb that a man is as good as his word.

Weltanschauung, regardless of its character, may exist in various degrees of awareness and formulation. To reach its maximum effectiveness in the integration of personality it must reach a corresponding level of consciousness. The function of consciousness is that of integration. Religion at its best has been much concerned to give form and expression to its Weltanschauung and has done this through creeds and beliefs, as well as in activities. Properly used, creeds and beliefs serve a vital need in personality development and integration. Improperly used, they serve purposes that in the end lead to personality illness. In its most creative periods, Christianity has utilized powerful word symbols for the expression of its faith. The dynamic relationship between verbal expression and inner reality itself was utilized to express the relation between truth and its expression, and the Bible became the "Word of God," and in the interpretation of St. John, Jesus became the "Logos of God." In its less creative moods, Christianity has taken refuge behind word symbols, and has made out of its creeds veritable ghosts of once living truth. In this it becomes much like the mentally sick individual who accepts his own inner ghosts as realities.

Religious symbols are the structure through which the religious Weltanschauung is formulated and expressed. A living religious creed, therefore, represents the structuralization of function. As on the physiological level, so in regard to the personality as a whole, function cannot be considered apart from structure. They are two aspects of the life process, which is constantly aiming at goals and seeking concrete realization of those aims. To live is to function in one direction or another; but function requires structure, and structure is meaningless apart from function. Religious symbols are a structure through which experiences on all levels of the life of the organism are expressed according to their meaning for the organism as a whole. They are a means through which every phase of experience may find a more or less permanent organization in terms of the meaning of experience to the whole personality in its total relationships.

For this reason the content of religious symbols may be as varied as the content of human experience. Some persons are shocked to discover that sexual feelings may find expression in religious symbols, even though the erotic element in some hymns is as glaring as it is in some modern jazz. This shock, of course, is related to personal attitudes of guilt, on the one hand, and to a failure to comprehend the relation of religious symbols to human experience, on the other. For religious symbols, being channels through which the total life of the organism finds expression, are universal and inclusive. There is no impulse, feeling, striving, idea, or conception of meaning that may not find expression in religious symbols. This is not a weakness in religion. It is the genius of religion to organize these diverse elements of personality and direct their expression toward meaningful goals. The Christian creeds have dealt with no inner problem that is not to be found in flesh and blood on the wards of any mental hospital.

Emotional, intellectual, and conative elements in experience find expression in various combinations in religious symbols. The emotional content of religious symbols needs more attention today than the intellectual, since much of the ineffectiveness of modern Christianity grows out of the over-emphasis on the intellectual content to the neglect of the emotional. And the emotional content is highly important in considering the relation of religion to health and disease.

The diversity of elements that may enter into the content of religious symbols is both a strength and a weakness. There is always a tendency for some element to gain more than its proper place in religious expression. Needs intensified by frustration may become a dominant influence, even to the point of controlling the whole religious outlook. This is illustrated in the experience of Mary Jones. The integration of personality through religious symbols is never completed; it is a continuing process subject to the strain and stress constantly arising in human experience. It is also subject to environmental influences, in terms of either religious or secular cultural patterns and values.

Religion, being concerned with the individual's relation to his universe, aims not only at personal integration, but also at integration with the group. As we have seen, these two aspects of integration go hand in hand. The Weltan-schauung of religion is not a private matter; it is a common possession of a group. Religious symbols, therefore, become the structure through which the religious fellowship functions. The powerful social support that is given to religious attitudes is a stabilizing force for members of the religious group. The content of religious symbols is influenced and enriched by experiences on the group level. Cultural as well as individual conflict finds expression through religious symbols. The aspirations and ideals of the group are woven into the religious structure. Religious symbols, always simple in themselves, may carry a content that is complex and contains both personal and cultural components.

This diversity of content in religious symbols has led to various interpretations of religion which are false because they are partial. A common illustration of this is the interpretation offered by certain psychoanalysts. They trace religion back to some hidden processes in the unconscious mind. The need for God is thus the expression of a failure to outgrow the helpless dependency on the parent in childhood. That unconscious factors enter prominently into religious symbolism no open-minded student of the problem would deny. But to interpret the entire religious content in those terms is to neglect an important function of the human mind and of religion. For creative religion is not the result of any one aspect of the mind; it is the expression of the whole person. It can be properly understood only from the point of view of the total relationships of the individual, not in terms of any part. And when looked at in this light, the direction given to the expression of partial patterns, such as unconscious impulses, takes on a significance equal at least to that of the impulse itself. Not only the roots of life, but the fruits are important, and a complete interpretation of religion must include each in its proper relationships.

THE NATURE AND FUNCTION OF RELIGIOUS BELIEF

Religious symbols of the action, object, color, and sound varieties are woven into religious ritual. Word symbols are woven into creeds and beliefs. Creeds are sometimes called "a confession of faith," and this, when the content is vital and the words not mere formula, is an apt expression. A living confession of faith, be it couched in conventional religious symbols or otherwise, is a formulation of the meaning of inner experience. It is an attempt to express symbolically what the individual has directly experienced in his total relationships. Truth of this kind is always the result of direct experience, and meaning is apprehended by faith and understanding rather than by logic. Religious beliefs are the formulation of the meaning and value, rather than of the facts, of human experience.

Being the structuralization of inner experience, creeds and beliefs raise meanings to a conscious level, even though all the components of experience may not be conscious. In this structuralization inner conflicts and tensions play an important role, as they create the problem for which meaning is the solution. Creeds and beliefs, though expressed in rational form, derive their content from every phase of the life of the organism, and they structuralize the tendencies and reactions which are in control or are in conflict.

Beliefs, and this is true of any belief, are as important for the integration and growth of personality as is the nervous system. Just as the nervous system binds the various physical organs into a whole, so dynamic beliefs bind the individual person with all his diverse tendencies into a whole. They go a step further, for to the extent that they are accepted by a group they become an important element in the structure of society and in the integration of individuals within society.

Beliefs, whether about facts or meanings, are important because of the role they play in adaptation to both the internal and the external environment. The belief that the world is flat; that disease is a punishment from God and, therefore, should not be interfered with by man; that the Old Testament account of creation is true and evolution is false—these and countless other beliefs have not only crystallized and guided the experiences of the generation in which they developed; they have been a structure determining the religious life and thinking of later generations. Beliefs involving relationships of man to man have played an especially important part, both constructive and destructive, in both group and individual welfare. The significance of beliefs goes far beyond the question of logical truth; it involves the question of life and death of the individual and the group. Many individual and social crises turn on the adequacy or the inadequacy of belief. The problem of health involves the sanity of belief as well as the soundness of body. Today there is no more important problem in the field of health, social welfare, and religion than that of the adequacy of belief for the solution of the human problem.

The relation of delusion to belief should not be over-looked. Delusion is usually defined as a false belief, but this means little or nothing in terms of its significance in personality. A false belief may exist because man has not yet mastered facts in terms of ideas. Thus the idea that the world is flat is a false belief. But false beliefs also grow out of the failure to achieve in experience meanings that are a basis for inner satisfaction, integration, and growth. Such false beliefs or delusions do not assist in adaptation to reality. Regardless of the question of logical truth, a belief that has its foundation in experience and expresses dominant elements in the personality structure carries a strong sense of reality. Such beliefs cannot be changed without first changing experience. A logical approach to such beliefs, whether delusional or not, is fruitless, as the basis of the belief is much deeper than logic. The psychology of belief and of delusion is identical at many points; the differences lie in the content, the purpose for which they are used, and the resulting effects on the personality.

A delusion, like any belief concerning meaning, is held because it performs a function in the life of the individual and because its contents are particularly real and valid to the individual who holds them. A delusion is always the product of a struggle for adaptation to the environment or some aspect of the environment—a struggle that has hurt the individual in an irreparable manner. As Campbell says: "Delusion, like fever, is to be looked on as part of nature's attempt at cure, an endeavor to neutralize some disturbing factor, to compensate for some handicap, to reconstruct a working contact with the group, which will still satisfy special needs."[1] White compares delusions to scar tissue on the somatic level. "It is the indication of the disease that has been and the destruction which was wrought as a result and the effort of repair, which was only partially successful and has left in this instance the mind scarred just as at the somatic level the body is left scarred."[2]

Belief, whether a delusion or not, is a crystallization. in

spoken and written words, of the life experience of the individual and the group. Beliefs vary because individual and social experience varies, not because of basic intellectual difficulties. The dynamic sources of beliefs go much deeper than the intellect. Indeed, most of the so-called intellectual difficulties in beliefs are symptomatic of deeper problems in the emotional life or in personality adjustments and relationships. Dynamic tendencies within the personality are crystallized in belief, and a conflict within the personality may be expressed in a conflict in beliefs. Intellectual doubt may be symptomatic of emotional conflict.

On the other hand, beliefs resting on an unstable personality adaptation may be developed into a logic-proof structure. Indeed, such structure may give unstable personalities a certain security and strength which must be constantly reinforced by the logical and systematic elaboration of the beliefs. But what seems logical to such persons may appear illogical to others. The crux of the problem is not in the logical development, but in the main premise, which represents the personality maladjustment in intellectual terms. Patients suffering from delusions of persecution are experts in building logical systems on a premise that is subjectively real but objectively false, without recognizing the true nature of their premise and its relation to their personality problem. But this is not confined to paranoid patients!

What we have said of belief in general is true of religious belief. Religion, as we have said, offers man a way of life. It involves man's total relationships, not merely one aspect of these relationships. It has to do, therefore, with those issues and problems central in man's experience, the solution to which affects his total being and determines his ultimate destiny. Religious beliefs are the formulation of these answers in the spoken and written word, in so far as man has been able to formulate answers. Religious beliefs are, therefore, not statements of fact, as they are frequently considered; they are interpretations of meaning. They embody man's insight into the nature of life—his own life and the life of the universe—and are the outgrowth of direct experience. They may be organized and criticized by reason, but a purely intellectual belief is impotent at the point of personality integration. Religious beliefs are not purely intellectual; they involve deeper aspects of the personality, as well as reason.

From the point of view of health and illness, the most important problem in regard to religious beliefs is not their logical truth, but their functional significance. Two persons may clothe their beliefs in the same symbols, one expressing a healthy and the other an unhealthy Weltanschauung. Religious beliefs may crystallize personality or cultural tendencies that function in the direction either of health or of disease. Strong internal pressures such as anxiety may lead a person to place extreme emphasis on a particular belief or to oversystematize his beliefs. The stronger the structure, the greater the security to be derived from it. A desire to force a particular belief on to others is also symptomatic of anxiety. The destruction of a belief may result in a serious disturbance within the personality.

Belief, religious or otherwise, is not only the expression of the Weltanschauung of the individual; it serves the same function for the group. Through common beliefs, individuals are integrated into groups. Religion necessarily involves the relation of the individual to others and religious beliefs grow out of and influence this relationship. Belief thus serves the important function of socialization on the level of attitudes and meanings. When the group loses sight of this functional significance, and the beliefs in themselves assume major importance, forces are set in motion to eliminate doubt and enforce common agreement. When the life of the group is threatened by an external force, beliefs become a rallying point and membership in the group is conditioned by agreement in common beliefs. In the group, as in the individual, the functional significance of belief is more important for health and illness than is logical truth. The present world conflict is symptomatic of the glaring inadequacy of the beliefs around which our culture is built.

Reference to the experience of Mary Jones will give point to this discussion. That the illness of this girl is not due to any one factor, but is rather the result of her total reaction to life, should be clear. Because she was so articulate, we have some insight into her basic attitude toward life, which is perhaps best characterized as one of childish dependency and helplessness in the face of an external environment that was terrifying. The place of conflict in her experiences and her attempt to formulate a solution for that conflict are apparent. Throughout her writing she is struggling with the problem of meaning and value, and is seeking a basis for a more satisfying relationship.

Mary formulated her Weltanschauung in religious symbols. Religion definitely presented a way of life to her, and she could not reconcile this with her inner impulses or with external pressures. Her impulses and certain external pressures conflicted seriously with her conscience and other external pressures. Between the conflicting tendencies stood her conscious ego, seeking to formulate a solution that would bring harmony. She was absorbed in the problem of finding salvation.

This girl failed to find a solution to her problem that would integrate her personality. Yet in the early pages of her diary the desire to do this is clear. Some of the reasons for this failure will be discussed later. Here we are merely pointing out the fact that she was struggling to bring order out of chaos; in other words, to find a creative solution for her problem. Such a solution would have resulted in a true religious experience, and a strengthening of her weak ego. But the pressure of the conflict was too strong, and her ego became submerged by impulses she had sought to repress. Rather than finding a basis for growth, she solved her problem in a regressive way, which involved an escape from hard reality.

That there was a strong erotic content in Mary's religious symbols cannot be denied. She saw "spiritual" and "sensual" forces in her nature warring against each other. Yet there was other content. Through the symbol "God" was expressed her basic attitude toward life and her dependency on outside powers to solve her problem. The problem of right and wrong and of her relationship to other people also found expression in her religious symbols. A conflict such as she faced has ramifications for the whole personality. A conflict that absorbed so much of her energy would naturally dominate her religious symbolism. This does not mean that her sickness is due to religion any more than it is due to sex. Actually it is the result of a failure to integrate the diverse elements of her personality, and to find a satisfying relation to internal and external reality.

Entirely missing in the account of her struggle is any reference to a meaningful relationship to a religious group. There are references to the efforts of some of her friends to talk her out of her belief about love. But she apparently struggled within herself without any significant contact with a church group. She felt very much isolated from the religious group, and hence failed to find the security and socialization that such a group could have given.

In this girl we see a good illustration of the functional significance of belief and of the inadequacy of her beliefs. The rigidity of her conscience as formulated in her ideas of right and wrong; her tendency to overidealize life, as formulated in her ideas of beauty and truth; her anxiety and guilt, which led her to view sex as evil; her tendency to withdraw from harsh reality into a dream world—all were expressed in her religious beliefs. To have dealt with her beliefs on the basis of logic would have been futile, as they were the expression of forces much deeper than her reason. As her illness developed, her beliefs became more bizarre because more primitive impulses were finding expression in them. Her strong need for socialization found expression in her desire to do religious work. Her sex conflict found a symbolic solution in her belief that a young man was called by God to devote his life with her in religious work. This would permit the idealized relation with men which she desired.

As for the physical side, this was completely denied, as she believed that her body was gone.

To Mary Jones, as to most mental patients, these symbols possessed a certain sense of reality. But this reality could not be communicated to other minds; more accurately, she was unable to communicate the meaning of the symbol to others because she had not clearly grasped it herself. Actually there was a strong tendency to conceal the meaning even from herself, and this was in a measure responsible for her illness. But religious symbols always refer to something beyond themselves, to realities in the inner or the external world of man. Health lies in the direction of preserving this objective reference through the gradual expansion of insight into the meaning of the symbol. Thus one function of religious symbols is that of promoting insight into those areas of experience which are only dimly, if at all, sensed. But in many mentally ill persons there is an awareness of the fact that their thought is struggling with some realities beyond their ability to grasp. They become ill because they cannot grasp enough of the kind of realities that preserve integration, or balance, or because they are too much absorbed with realities that have a disintegrating effect. The high goal of religious thought is to grasp in an ever-increasing measure that order of existence which is written into the very function and structure of life itself, and without devotion to which wholeness cannot be achieved. The difference between the religious genius and the mentally ill person is that the genius is able to express life experience in symbols having a universal and timeless significance, and is furthermore able to grasp, at least to a measure, the pattern of life leading to wholeness and having validity for all men. Function and structure in religion cannot be divorced from function and structure in personality.

REFERENCES

1. CAMPBELL, C. M., *Delusion and Belief*, p. 9. Cambridge, 1927.
2. WHITE, W. A., *Medical Psychology*, p. 123. New York, 1931.

CHAPTER VIII

SYMBOLISM AND REALITY IN RELIGIOUS EXPERIENCE

SYMBOLS are the means through which religion formulates its answers to questions involving the nature of the universe and the destiny of man. The tendency to formulate and structuralize is inherent in life; all function involves a structure. Religious symbols are forms through which man has expressed his insight into the nature and meaning of life and through which he has structuralized this insight into a way of living. In this chapter we shall discuss certain aspects of the nature and function of religious symbols which are important in a consideration of the relation of religion and health.

THREE KINDS OF THOUGHT AND THEIR SYMBOLS

The capacity to symbolize is synonymous with the capacity to think, as thought is clothed in symbols. Different kinds of thinking utilize symbols in different ways. Religious thought itself may aim at different goals and will, therefore, use religious symbols in different ways. This difference may determine whether religious thought and symbols are utilized for the purposes of health or of illness. Further discussion of these problems is needed.

There is, first, a kind of thought that has for its purpose the manipulation of some external aspect of the environment, or of dealing with ideas of a factual nature derived from the personality or the environment. The bulk of everyday thinking through which man seeks to organize and adapt himself to his physical environment or this environment to himself is of this kind. The basic requirement of symbols in which such thought is clothed is that they literally and accurately represent the object for which they stand.

Literal representation is a matter of exact definition based on superficial or arbitrary considerations, without reference to any inherent, underlying relationships. Historical factors which influenced the development of a particular symbol may be entirely forgotten without changing or diminishing the literal significance of the symbol. Thus the main requisite for this kind of communication is a common understanding of the meaning of the symbol, and for word symbols the chief source of such understanding is the dictionary. Most mathematical and scientific symbols serve this kind of thinking, as do symbols used in psychoanalysis. To Freud, symbols are forms through which unconscious feelings and ideas are expressed, particularly in dreams, and the meaning of a symbol is determined by comparison in such characteristics as form and appearance between the symbol and its object. Thus an elongated object such as a gun may symbolize the male sexual organ. That the unconscious may be expressed in such literal symbols is not to be denied. But symbol, as we are using the term in relation to religious thought, is a means of expressing insights into relationships and values that concern the whole personality, and the true development of religious symbols is governed more by conscious than by unconscious factors. Religious thought and symbols may and do degenerate to the level where they become largely the expression of unconscious elements in the personality or where they are used in a literal significance, but this is a sign of illness in religion rather than health.

A second kind of thought has for its purpose the description of some object or aspect of experience in terms of some other sense experience. The symbols through which this kind of thought is expressed must bear an inherent relationship to the object or experience symbolized. This relationship is based, not on external characteristics, but on some quality common to both the reality and the symbol and on which thought is being focused. Thus we may say that an object is as hard as a rock, or as cold as ice, or that a man is tiger-like. Such thought may be clothed, not only in words, but in symbols of form and color, such as a painting descriptive of the beauty of a landscape. In descriptive thought there is no attempt to interpret meaning on any level other than that of sense experience. However, it usually emphasizes some quality of an object. Thus to describe a person as mouselike is to single out a particular quality of his personality, and to present that quality in vivid form. Glazunov's symphony, "The Seasons," is a description in sound that enhances even the beauty of nature.

It will be readily seen that descriptive thinking differs from literal thinking in one important aspect. The symbols used in literal thinking have no inherent association with reality, but are rather selected arbitrarily or on the basis of external comparison. In descriptive thinking the association between object and symbol is inherent. When this relationship is destroyed the symbol becomes useless as a tool of descriptive thought. If a mouselike person suddenly becomes aggressive, a new symbol is required for accurate apprehension and expression. The resemblance between object and symbol must remain or descriptive thinking becomes nonsense.

Religious thought is neither of the literal nor of the descriptive variety, but falls into a third group. The function of religious thought is that of penetrating beneath the level of appearance and sense experience to discover fundamental meanings and relationships. Such thought uses its symbols for the purpose of apprehending and expressing insight or understanding of the nature and aim of life as experienced by the individual and group. It proceeds on the assumption that the inner world of man and his relationships with the larger universe are founded on orderly principles which man himself does not create but only may discover and accept as a basis for ordering his life. Religious thought thus deals with realities that are just as inescapable as is the law of gravitation. It deals not with one aspect of experience, but with life as a whole. Meaning and value are not discovered in isolated experiences, but by considering their relationship to the whole of experience. While literal thought deals with external realities with an economical expenditure of time and energy, religious thought seeks to apprehend goals and values around which personality may be integrated. Such thought and its symbols utilize the synthetic functions of the mind, while literal symbols serve more the processes of analysis. It is through the synthetic rather than the analytic mental processes that meanings which are capable of producing integration and wholeness are achieved.

In creative religious thought there is an inherent association between the reality and the symbol. The symbol is useful because it is a tangible form which, at least to a measure, expresses an intangible but dynamic truth. Religious symbols are drawn from the whole realm of man's external world, but they become alive and meaningful only as they express some reality of man's inner world. Nature is replete with objects and processes which serve as symbols of realities and processes in man's inner life. Thus light and darkness are common attributes of nature having a literal meaning. They may also be used descriptively. But in religious thought light may become a symbol for the understanding of meaning and values that removes ignorance and fear, and gives man a basis on which to order his life. In such usage the inherent relationship between symbol and reality is maintained, and such thought serves the function of integration and growth. But unless this association is maintained, religious thinking becomes only the manipulation of symbols, and the light becomes darkness. Such thought leads to illness.

For further consideration of the function of thought in relation to its symbols, one symbol such as water may be used. The word "water" may be used quite literally so that even a child can grasp the full meaning. Descriptively, we may say that something is as tasteless as water, or that it appears to the eye as water. This is to describe, not water, but some other object through reference to some quality of water. In religious thought a person may grasp some meaning or value that leads to security and peace, and express it thus: "He leadeth me beside the still waters." Or he may grasp some reality that brings deep satisfaction and renews hope, and may express this through some symbol such as "the living water." But such symbols are not to be taken literally or on the level of sense experience. So taken they lose their true function in personality and become absurd. Jesus was a master in the use of insight symbols as vehicles to express his grasp of realities leading to wholeness. His parables are insight symbols that penetrate beneath the level of experience to fundamental laws and relationships.

But religious symbols may be and are taken literally. When this occurs, the dynamic relationship between symbol and inner reality is lost, and the symbol is given a literal meaning. It then becomes powerless to effect new integrations within the personality and becomes a means of promoting unhealthy tendencies. An illustration of this is the literal interpretation of the creation story in Genesis, which places it on a level and in conflict with the scientific theory of evolution. An arbitrary and exact meaning cannot be given to religious symbols without destroying their true religious function. The scientific account of religion does just this, as does much theology. While such formulations have a value, it is not at the point of the integration of personality. Theology, for example, is frequently described as being "dry," which means that through arbitrary definition the living reality that is religion has been pressed out of its symbols.

Neither can religious symbols be utilized as descriptive symbols without destroying their true function. When properly used, religious symbols do not function on the level of sense experience. But they may be improperly used as descriptive symbols. The description of the life hereafter in terms of pearly gates and golden streets is an example of this. Descriptions of the religious life in terms of sensuous love is another example. Some mystics employ such descriptive symbols to portray their experiences. This may occur in persons who are severely frustrated in their physical love life. While religious symbols necessarily operate through the senses, they express realities beneath the level of sense experience.

Religious thought and its symbols are means of gaining insight into the fundamental laws and relationships which give life meaning and on which a way of life may be formulated. But religious thought and symbols may degenerate to the place where they are used primarily for the purposes of evasion and concealment. When this occurs, light becomes darkness, and processes leading to illness rather than to health develop. A discussion of this problem is reserved for Chapter IX.

THE DYNAMIC RELATION BETWEEN SYMBOL AND REALITY

Basic to an understanding of religious symbols is an appreciation of the dynamic relation of the symbol to the meaning or reality symbolized. In living religious symbols this relationship involves an association between the reality and the symbol that is inherent in the nature of each. For example, food symbols such as bread and water are common in religion. Such symbols are living and vital when they express the idea that in some experience involving the individual's relationships he has found meaning and values which give renewed strength and stability through the satisfaction of inner needs. These values are analogous to the value of food and water to the physical body. Thus the symbols "bread of life" and "living water" are forms through which the believer may express meanings or relationships contributing to the continued integration and enrichment of personality and preventing disintegration in the face of conflict. But they function in this way only when the idea presented by the symbol bears an intrinsic association with a reality in the experience of the individual. In all vital religion there is an organic relation between the symbol and the reality symbolized; between structure and meaning. In formalistic religion, the reality is missing, and hence such religion is ineffectual in promoting growth and integration.

Because of the intrinsic and dynamic association between living religious symbols and the reality for which they stand, their use is governed not by logic, but by analogy. Properly understood and used, the language of religion does not say: this is literally that; because of this, therefore that is true. Religious symbols and scientific symbols differ in their essential nature. The one conveys an experience of meaning; the other connotes a fact. The language of religion does not seek to express causality; it expresses finality, purpose and value. When an inner reality is grasped through the use of a religious symbol, the reason may and should be employed to evaluate that reality in terms of its significance for personality and to relate it to other experiences. We are suffering today, however, from an attempt to reason a meaning into religious symbols, or to rethink religion in order to find reality. This cannot be done in a manner that creates personality integration. If meanings are not present in the experience of a person, they cannot be effectually created by reason. Thus a person may reason that religious symbols should have a certain meaning, but in all honesty know that this meaning is not present. Or a person may mistake either a superficially accepted or carefully reasoned meaning for the deeper experience of meaning, and find that the former are impotent to integrate his personality or to give inner stability at a time of stress. The reality of religious symbols grows out of an intrinsic association between the experience and the form of expression, an association grasped by insight or by faith. Insight and faith are functions of the whole personality, not of a part. The emotional and conative aspects of personality, as well as the intellectual, find expression in religious faith, and are always involved in the dynamic association between symbol and reality.

The language of religion seeks to express something that is fundamentally real in the inner life of the believer through an analogy with something that is real in his external life.

That symbols express this reality inadequately is recognized by the truly religious person; yet symbolism is the only way in which truth may be apprehended. Human experience is many-sided, and a body of symbols that is both diverse and rich is necessary for its organization and expression and for that reconciliation of opposites essential to the solution of conflict and to the attainment of truth. It is also necessary in order that symbols expressing different aspects of experience may correct each other and thereby maintain a balance in the expression of diverse elements of the personality. Symbols which express inner security and peace, for example, need to be balanced by symbols expressing a sense of responsibility and self-direction, lest overemphasis on the symbols of security foster feelings of dependence and helplessness that injure the personality. In the experience of Mary Jones, we see the use of a one-sided symbolism which prevents the much-needed development of other essential elements of the personality. Reason may function at the point of discovering a lack of balance in symbolism; but it cannot create living verbal symbols any more than it can create a Sistine Madonna. For the formulation of a way of life is an art involving the ability first to find meaning and then to express that meaning in living symbols. In this process the imagination plays an important role.

The principle of analogy is fundamental in religious symbolism. Religion, having to do with the relation of the finite and the Infinite, proceeds on the principle that an understanding of the laws and relationships in the realm of the finite leads to an understanding of the laws and relationships in the realm of the Infinite. To the religious mind, the finite is but the expression of the Infinite. It is on the basis of this principle that many religious doctrines, for example, that of the Incarnation, find their significance; the life of the finite being an expression of and revealing the life of the Infinite. Just as science has discovered that certain natural laws are equally applicable in the realm of the atom or of the astronomical universe, so religion operates on the principle that laws that govern the inner life of man, the microcosm, are the same as the laws that govern his external universe, the macrocosm. The religious person feels himself as part of a larger unity, and life processes within his own inner world become analogous to life processes in this larger unity. Either man, though finite, is an organic part of the Infinite, to which he has to adjust, adjustment in this case meaning the attainment of harmony, or he is an isolated bundle of life-possessing cells having no organic relation with his universe. The former is fundamental in the religious view of life and is expressed in the organismic view of life; the latter is being denied by modern scientific discoveries in so far as they support the concept of the organismic view of life. Religious symbols are, therefore, a means through which man expresses his relation to the Infinite in terms derived from finite experience, the only source available to him. The principle of immanence is essential to an understanding of the nature of reality and symbol in religion.

It is only through a grasp of the Infinite as it is revealed in finite experience, that man can maintain a perspective which avoids megalomania, on the one hand, or utter despair, on the other. For both megalomania and despair spring from the same root—the failure to find an Absolute that gives balance and significance to the relative. Finding no Absolute that gives meaning to his smallness, man may deify himself and become a god. "There is no God," says Nietzsche, "for if there were a god how could I endure it to be no god?" But such deification always fails to produce peace, or lasting satisfaction. It is an artificial inflation of the ego, which is sooner or later shattered by stern reality. The reaction to this is one of despair, rationalized in the belief that the universe has no concern for human values. Chronic pessimism is symptomatic of an injured ego that has not been allowed to heal. Religion is always faced with the problem of maintaining a vital relationship between the finite and the Infinite, between man's ego and that larger Reality which man cannot with impunity ignore and on which he is dependent for his very life.

Religion has always sought to apprehend and express man's

relation to Ultimate Reality through insight symbols. God has been the symbol for that Ultimate, at least in Christianity. The Christian religion has not sought to raise man by his own bootstraps, or to bring salvation by the mere manipulation of psychological processes. It has sought to relate finite man significantly to the Infinite, or to the Whole of which he is only a small part. The symbol "God" has been elaborated by many other symbols, each of which has expressed some aspect of reality that man can co-operate with but cannot avoid or fight against without peril. Thus God is Creative Power, God is Love, God is Light, God is a Heavenly Father, God is Reason, God is the Highest Social Value, God is Law, according to which aspect of reality is of greater significance to a personality at a given time. Man has indeed made God in his own image because he has had no other image with which to work. But it must be remembered that the image itself is only a representation of a Reality without which man himself would not exist. Anthropomorphism becomes a problem in religion only when the dynamic relation between symbol and reality is destroyed and the image becomes Reality. Theism and humanism are equally susceptible to this error in symbolism. Man finds his truest conception of the Ultimate in his truest insight into his own experience, regardless of the symbol by which this is expressed. The dynamic force of the Christian symbol "God" may be seen in the fact that to comprehend its reality requires not so much the exercise of reason as a continuous reorientation of life toward some reality that produces growth within the personality.

RELIGIOUS SYMBOLS AND MAN'S MASTERY OF HIMSELF AND HIS WORLD

Man's fundamental problem is that of working out between himself and his world a relationship that will provide a basis for his self-preservation, psychological as well as physical, and self-realization. The extent to which he fails to do this makes him a prey to disease processes of various kinds.

For the purposes of self-preservation and self-realization, a degree of mastery over both himself (his inner world) and his external world is required. This mastery is not to be thought of in terms of repression of some inner impulse, a method all too frequently used and one which leads to unhealthy results. It involves rather an achievement of a measure of conscious understanding of the nature and aim of life and of the conditions necessary for realization. It also involves an understanding of oneself and one's world, which makes possible changes that are necessary in either for the achievement of desirable ends, on the one hand, or adaptation, without an unhealthy amount of tension, to inner or external realities which cannot be changed, on the other. Such mastery rests on the individual's understanding of the nature of both himself and his world.

Modern man has achieved a certain amount of understanding and mastery of his external world through science. This mastery has been more effective in relation to man's external world than to his inner world, though the psychological sciences are working on this latter problem. Man's mastery of his external world may be described as the successful manipulation of certain areas of the physical universe for his own ends, through a knowledge of the laws governing those areas. But many areas of the physical universe remain to be mastered by science. Science has pushed back our horizons and has introduced us to even greater problems that it has solved.

Considering man's welfare, the question arises; For what ends or purposes has man gained such a degree of mastery over the physical universe? Certainly in answer to this question we must say that man's mastery of his world has given him many tools for the kind of self-destruction that is inevitable because he has not mastered himself. Forty years ago Freud incurred the wrath of many of his contemporaries by telling them that the basis of many of their self-destructive tendencies, that is, their tendencies to fall ill, was to be found in an unwise use of their love and sex potentialities. Later Freud, and especially some of his followers, pointed to man's capacity to be aggressive and hostile and to his general failure to master this phase of his life as another source of self-destructive tendencies. The degree in which science has succeeded in mastering the physical universe has given man a tool—a tool for his self-realization or self-destruction, individually and collectively. Science as such has been and is powerless to determine which end its achievements shall serve.

Even in the realm of personality this is true. A scientific understanding of personality or of one's inner life does not guarantee a more healthy existence. The use an individual makes of whatever understanding of himself he has been able to achieve is determined by his basic attitudes and the meaning or values he has set for himself, by what he really wants out of life, in short, by his Weltanschauung. Such understanding may be used for self-justification or self-realization.

Science, then, affords man a kind of mastery of his world and of himself. It gives him techniques by which he may achieve at least some of his goals. But techniques are not enough. To these must be added the meaning or purpose for which they are used, the values achieved through them. This involves the personality as a whole and can be expressed only through symbols embodying man's basic orientation toward the Whole of which he is only a small part. Religion —or, to be more specific, the religion of Jesus—offers an orientation that has as its central aim the constructive mastery of life. True, those professing this religion have all too frequently given it expressions that are destructive of human values, rather than constructive, and this tendency will be discussed later.

The kind of mastery that is attained through science and the kind attained through religion are different in another way that is important for health. The factual knowledge and techniques of science may be passed on from one generation to another through the process of intellectual education. The symbols and structure of religion may be passed on in the same way, and alas, some religious education is all too proficient at this point. It succeeds in effecting a dissociation between the intellectual elements and the deeper dynamic content of religious symbols. The deeper meaning and values of religion, the attitudes and relationships resulting in integration and in a sense of unity with others, the Weltanschauung, cannot be passed on through purely intellectual procedures. They are achieved only through experiences that involve the whole person and all of his relationships. They are in part the result of identification with other people and groups. Thus the relationships created by a parent may have a much greater influence on the child's religious life than all the formal religious education to which he may be subjected. In the final analysis, each individual must work out the meaning of life in his own experience. This cannot be passed on to him. Whatever inner mastery a person attains, he does so through the exercise and growth of his own powers, in close relationship with his external world.

The kind of mastery that is conducive to health is the product of growth. Complete mastery cannot be expected of a child or an adolescent, but is rather a characteristic of the mature personality. The process of growth is an essential characteristic of personality, and is an expression of the function of individuation. It is as important, or even more important, that a child's capacity for finding new and deeper meanings in life expands as it is for his body to grow. We are learning today that failure on the level of meaning may result in failure on the physical and social levels. Only through such inner growth can the potentialities of personality be developed and man can gain mastery over himself. It is those parts not properly developed and properly related to the whole personality that succeed in gaining a dominant position over the whole, and which interfere with self-mastery.

The idea of growth on the physical level is quite obvious and readily accepted by most people. But the idea of growth in the personality is more difficult to the average person. The principle of training a child in the way he should go has often been interpreted in a mechanical, static sense that implied pressing the personality into a definite groove rather than creating conditions that make possible the development of the child's potentialities along constructive lines. This has been a source of much harm to growing personalities. Many adults find themselves unhappily in the grip of patterns into which they were forced during childhood, and these frustrate their creative urges.

The relation of religious growth to personality growth receives a great deal of lip service in religious circles, but little attempt is made to define this relationship specifically. The tendency to expect children to function on the basis of adult religious ideas is indicative. Children can be taught religious symbols and can be given some conception of what those symbols mean to others. They can be helped to interpret their own experience in terms of symbols that have a common meaning for the group. But if the child is told that a certain symbol must mean thus and so, and is left with the impression that he must accept this meaning, he may be placed in a conflict that in turn may lead either to injury to his personality or to the discarding of religion. Group pressure combined with the child's need to belong may force an outward acceptance of a symbol void of all inner meaning. This becomes a burden rather than a help to the child. And unless the child is helped to develop the meaning of his symbols in harmony with his expanding experience, they will function to retard his growth. The symbol "God," for example, may stand for the creative power within life, but if an individual's conception of this power and of his relationship to it remains the same at six, sixteen, and thirty-six, neurosis may result. The adult who remains infantile in his religious outlook will find that his impulses and environment both tend to master him and to enslave him. Sound religious education aims at helping the child develop a relationship with reality through which growth may take place. But this is much more a matter of creating conditions in which a child can find values pertinent to his inner needs, particularly in terms of personal relationships with other people, than of a formal training according to the best educational methods.

The essence of growth is the necessity and willingness to give up something in order to attain something higher. Psychoanalysis is quite clear on the dangers of what it calls fixations in one or another stage of emotional development, that is, of failure to grow. It finds that such failure may be due either to a failure to find satisfaction on a given level (frustration), which makes growth seem undesirable, or to experiences through which more than a healthy amount of satisfaction is derived, and hence the stimulus toward growth is removed. Of the latter, the spoiled child is a good example. In other words, growth of personality centers in the problem of the meaning of life and the necessity of developing relationships which make growth possible. To become mature, one must put away childish meanings and relationships; one must give up satisfactions on an earlier level for the sake of acquiring the ability to find satisfactions on a more mature level. Anyone observing a growing child sees him giving up some activity which meant a great deal to him as he learns new activities and develops new interests. Expansion of the capacity to find meaning in life, even in the face of frustrations, is essential to his emotional and religious growth. But every step in this expansion involves the renunciation of a former satisfaction and meaning. This renunciation involves purely selfish goals for the sake of achieving goals in which another person or a group participates. In its true expression, it is not so much renunciation in the sense of crushing an impulse as it is in the sense of raising the expression of impulses to a higher social level. It is the infantile demand to find satisfaction without reference to the welfare of others that must be outgrown in order to achieve the kind of mastery that leads to wholeness.

The idea of growth through renunciation of lesser personal aims is inherent in the Christian religion. The principle of sacrifice is the expression of this idea. This was highly elaborated in the symbolism of the Hebrews. Other elements crept into this symbolic act, but the fundamental principle is there. In Jesus we see it reach its highest expression as a conscious principle of life. "He that findeth his life shall lose it; and he that loseth his life for my sake shall find it." This is the basis of the growth that, paradoxically enough, leads to self-mastery. For either one masters himself in terms of the expression of his impulses toward goals that lead beyond himself, or one is mastered by impulses that turn in on the self because they have no larger goal. Without such renunciation there can be only that failure to grow which confuses repression with mastery or undirected expression with freedom, and which leads to illness in one form or another.

Insight symbolism, or the structure of religion, serves an important function in the process of growth. Growth is always from the known to the unknown, from what is mastered to that which remains to be mastered. Forms of expression which will indicate the direction and goal are essential. These forms must possess a certain stability and yet this must be balanced by a capacity to change as growth takes place. Rigidity and too high a degree of flexibility in symbolic religious structure are equal dangers. Religious structure should be capable of expressing the sum total of growth that has been achieved, but also should provide goals for further growth. Preoccupation with symbols expressing the idea of sin, for example, is indicative of an unhealthy rigidity, as such experiences are never stopping places in healthy religion. Such symbols express areas in which mastery has not taken place and their primary reference is to inner, psychological reality rather than to an external act. Preoccupation with them leads to failure in growth.

But there are areas of life which are eternally a part of the unknown in any scientific sense. The ultimate meaning of life, the answer to the problem of suffering, the meaning of death, the unescapable tragedy in human existence, are baffling to the intellect. The mind that is content to rest on what science can prove in regard to many such issues is thereby limiting the use of its ability to penetrate beneath appearances, and to express, in terms of insight symbols, a faith that gives stability and strength. Some insight into or faith concerning the unknown is essential to a Weltanschauung that really includes all the problems of life, and, therefore, to the higher levels of growth. Such insight or faith is the heart of religion.

The open-minded observer of sick people, whether of physical, mental or social sickness, cannot but be impressed by the fact that religious symbols do not always promote growth. He finds sick people in whom religion has functioned to prevent growth, and to reinforce regressive trends. This brings to light the paradoxical nature of religious symbols. On the one hand, they are means through which the human mind reaches out for new ideas and for a deeper orientation. On the other, they may be used to express the exact opposite purpose. Under the influence of strong conflict they may be used to conceal the expression of infantile or primitive ideas and to assist the personality back to a level that avoids conflict. But this is a perversion of their genuine function. As one student of the problem writes: "Symbols are the chief means by which the human mind expresses, not so much those ideas which it has outgrown or wishes to conceal, but those which it has not yet mastered." [1] Religious symbols, when properly used, function on the growing edge of personality. In the experience of Mary Jones, the regressive use of religious symbols came to predominate, as she found it impossible to outgrow her conflict. She tried to master life on the basis of repression of central impulses by a severe conscience; she was unable to master it in terms of understanding both impulses and conscience, and through a higher growth and integration than she had yet achieved. She had come to the place where the alternatives were clear-cut; either she must grow up or she must regress to mental illness. Her use of religious symbols served the regressive purpose.

THE PROBLEM OF REALITY IN RELIGION

The approach we have been making raises the question as to the objectivity and subjectivity of religion. Viewing religion in terms of function and structure will impress some as making it purely utilitarian, and neglecting its "objective realities." We shall not enter into the important question of the objective reality of religion in the philosophical sense. We shall rather deal with the question of reality as it is found in the experience of persons, and the function which an idea or its symbolic structure may serve in the personality.

Returning to some of our basic concepts, we see that the personality is the result of neither subjective nor objective factors alone. It is rather the result of a union of objective and subjective factors. Just as oxygen and hydrogen lose their individual identities when they become water, so the inner and external worlds lose their sharp distinctions in the personality. We would recall the fact that science has discovered provisions for spontaneity on the part of the organism, so that it is not merely a rubber stamp of its environment. On the other hand, the organism cannot exist without a fit environment. It also has within itself ability to act on its environment. From an ideal point of view, a balance between objective and subjective factors is desirable. This would mean that each would be given its proper place. Actually this probably never or seldom occurs. In some personalities objective factors play a predominant role, even to the extent of repressing vital impulses of the organism. In others, subjective factors play a predominant role, destroying or evading objective factors. Health requires that due consideration be given to both factors in the equation, and symptoms of illness will arise when the balance is thrown too far in either direction.

A Weltanschauung that serves to integrate the personality is a synthesis of subjective and objective factors as they find expression in meaning and value. To the extent that it is overbalanced in either direction it will tend toward disintegration and illness. The symbols of religion, in expressing the Weltanschauung, provide a basis for discovery of this balance or lack of balance. When symbols predominantly express either subjective or objective factors they do not function in the direction of health. In their true function, religious symbols express a synthesis of that which is within and that which is without. In them the subjective and the objective may be combined with utmost effectiveness.

In considering the reality of religion one meets two points: reality in terms of the content of the symbol and the sense of reality in the use of the symbol. The reality of religion, psychologically considered, is the reality of human experience as this is discovered and elaborated within the personality in terms of meaning. The life blood of religion is those experiences which nurture the personality and lead to self-realization in harmony with one's fellows and with the universe. Now, a thousand logical proofs of the existence of God as an objective reality would avail nothing without experiences which give the symbol "God" a meaning. The problem of philosophy may be the existence of God, but the problem of religion is that of the meaning of God. There is no symbol which better expresses the total meanings born out of man's synthesis of the subjective and objective than the symbol "God." The symbol "God" may mean to one person an oblong blur, to another an all-seeing Judge who punishes every misdoing, to another an indulgent old man up in the skies, and to another the source of energy and life and law. In all except the first, the sense of reality may be equally strong. To the extent that there is a feeling of reality, the symbol portrays a central psychological truth within the experience of the person, a truth that is one factor determining the outcome of the person's life. But a sense of reality in the symbol may prevent the person from becoming aware of the actual psychological content. By bringing this content to the level of consciousness at least to a measure, through the proper use of the symbol, the individual is in a position to evaluate it in terms of the ideas of others and of its influence in his own life. But danger is involved in confusing the sense of reality with reality itself.

At this point, the cultural side of religion plays a highly important role. The particular religious group to which a person belongs has its common interpretation of life and its common solution of life problems. In Christian groups these symbols center in Christ as the ideal. One task of religion, culturally considered, is to give the individual a basis for the evaluation of the meanings of his symbols and the solution of his conflict in terms of a group. Religion operates on the insight that the problems of the individual are also the problems of the race, and that the same principles apply in the solution of each. Included in this is the principle that the problems of the individual are never adequately solved in isolation from the group. Here again we see the integrating function of religion at work. Religion carries out this function by enabling the individual to engage in a group experience of a stimulating nature, and through techniques such as worship and prayer, which, at their best, seek to raise meaning to the level of consciousness and to effect a close association between symbol and reality. The religious group stimulates and guides the process of evaluation and integration. Thus religious symbols not only provide an expression of a synthesis of the inner and external worlds, but in the very development of religious structure a component of the external world, the religious group, plays a dynamic role. Vital relationship with a religious group is essential to a development of symbolism in a healthy manner. On the other hand, such a relationship is no guarantee of a healthy development. Other factors, such as the nature of the teachings of the group and personal tendencies which are unduly strong, must be taken into account.

One function of the religious group is to help the individual maintain a balance between the subjective and the objective. This task is not without its pitfalls. For the religious group that exerts too much authority and seeks to coerce the individual into certain beliefs or attitudes, regardless of what is happening within him, will in the end hamper if not block the development of maturity of personality. On the other hand, a group, like many liberal religious groups today, that has no very stable convictions or is confused, will offer the individual little security and assistance in the solution of his problem.

In thinking about reality in religious symbols, we must distinguish between a sense of reality and reality in terms of psychological content. The sense of reality in relation to any idea indicates that it portrays something psychologically true. On the other hand, the actual content of a symbol gives insight into dynamic factors within the personality of which it is an expression. There is, for example, a patient who thought of God and her father as being identical. At the age of thirty she thought of her father as she had at the age of six. God to her stood for a psychological truth portraying her relationship with her father at the age of six. At the age of thirty she felt that God strongly condemned her for having sexual relations with her husband. This feeling of condemnation was very real. Through the symbol "God" she was expressing a fundamental psychological process, but one which would inevitably produce illness rather than health.

The sense of reality is not a criterion on which the wholesomeness of a religious idea can be judged. We state this specifically because it is often made such a criterion by clergymen, and people are frequently told that in some way they should find a sense of the reality of God. In urging this, clergymen themselves have different conceptions of what the reality of God actually means and they are likely to leave a confused congregation more confused. The sense of the reality of God cannot be manufactured at will. When the symbol "God" becomes an effective means for the expression of a living process, it becomes real. The high function of religion is not so much that of urging men to develop a sense of reality in the symbol "God," but actually to help men find an experience that gives a meaning for which the symbol "God" is a worthy and living expression.

A major problem in regard to reality in religion is that involved in the dissociation between symbol and inner reality. People become ill when their religious symbols structuralize inner processes that make a healthy adjustment to life impossible. The patient cited above became ill because her particular God interfered with her marriage adjustment by creating guilt. Behind this process there is always a deeper one involving the association between symbol and reality. Previously it was pointed out that religious symbols fulfill their function of integration when the relation between the symbol and reality remains inherent and dynamic. It is possible for this dynamic relationship between symbol and reality to become dissociated, so that the meaning is repressed from consciousness. In this case the symbol itself becomes reality, and is taken literally. This happened to the patient discussed here. God, a literal being somewhere in the world, was condemning her for some "sin," the exact nature of which she did not consciously know, and was demanding that she be punished. The relation between this symbol and her life experiences was completely dissociated in consciousness. The symbol had become all-important and very real. But this made it impossible to deal constructively with crucial life experiences. It also prevented her growth and effective mastery of life. Because her God became dissociated from life processes, she fell ill. In a later chapter we shall deal more specifically with the process of dissociation.

The fact of dissociation between reality and symbol brings up another problem. It has been stated that when this occurs the symbol itself takes on a sense of reality. By investing the symbol with illusory reality, the individual rejects the reality of experience. Mary Jones so invested the symbol "love" with reality that she rejected love, the experience. The woman who thought God had condemned her rejected every constructive aspect of her experience. Another common expression of the same tendency is the denial of some reality on the basis of a "more real reality." Patients in a mental hospital are frequently heard to say that the physicians have no understanding of their cases, and that no one really understands their case except themselves. Their view of life is true; all other views are false. Religious persons have often denied the validity of science by holding that any concept which conflicts with religion is untrue because religion is the supreme truth. Fundamentalists, Modernists, and Catholics, not to mention many others, frequently defend their own views by resorting to a denial of the ability of other points of view to grasp reality in its completeness.

The greater the dissociation between symbols and meaning the greater the need of asserting their reality and of denying contrary views. He who thinks he is well does not need a physician to help him find some curative reality. He whose symbols lead to an understanding of his inner needs will welcome the revelation of a saving reality from whatever source. He has a humility and a reverence which lead him beyond the form to the reality. The true searcher for truth is not disturbed by symbols that conflict with his own symbols. For he is conscious of the inadequacy of his own symbols to apprehend truth completely, and also remembers that truth lies not in maintaining a one-sided point of view in the name of reality, but in that reconciliation of opposites which results in a creative solution of life's conflicts. The young woman who maintained an overly idealized view of love and denied the validity of its physical aspects became ill because she could not reconcile these opposites in a creative manner. The denial of reality, even in the name of reality, does not produce health.

The problem of reality in religion finds expression in

another set of symbols, those portraying the actual and those formulating the ideal. The psychiatrist, absorbed in the problem of adjustment of individuals to everyday experiences, thinks of actual situations as reality, and is often inclined to discount ideals as illusory. Because the problems which bring individuals to him are usually the expression of conflict situations, the psychiatrist tends to think of reality as conflict-producing experiences. The psychiatrist meets many individuals in whom a rigid conscience or a narrow conception of life is one element in their conflict and frequently a major factor in their illness. Some psychiatrists, in their treatment, tend to take sides in the conflict and champion the gratification of desires and the discarding of ideals. Psychiatrists are frequently criticized for seeking to adjust persons on what is considered to be a low level of reality.

Religion, on the other hand, tends to think of the reality in terms of the ultimate rather than in terms of the actual. This leads religion to stress ideals, goals, and values. To religion, these are reality. Religion is concerned not primarily with where man is today, but with where he is going and where he ought to go. On the other hand, religion, like psychiatry, becomes vitally concerned with the actual when it creates problems in relation to the ideal. The age-old question "What must I do to be saved?" implies an actuality out of which one needs to move in the direction of a more satisfying and creative life.

Religion and medicine are inclined to become impaled on the horns of a dilemma. Medicine, with its scientific approach, absorption with specific problems, and literal symbolic expression, is likely to overemphasize the actual and neglect the ideal. Yet a great deal of illness is due to the failure of ideals, and the ideal of health cannot be achieved without reference to other ideals. Religion, on the other hand, being concerned with the ultimate and expressing itself in insight symbols, is constantly in danger of overemphasizing the ideal and of neglecting the actual. Yet salvation can never be achieved without adequate consideration of the actual. A physician who denies the reality of ideals is just as much a pathogenic agent as the clergyman who denies the reality of an actual situation. Being hard-boiled about delicate life processes is just as dangerous as being sentimental. Nevertheless, the strength of medicine is in its emphasis on particulars and the strength of religion is in its emphasis on universals and values. In actual life, and properly conceived, these are not contradictory. They are two aspects of the total living process, and represent opposites which must be reconciled in experience in order to avoid the warping of personality. Such reconciliation is a continual process, and is never finally achieved. The task of religion is to provide a structure through which life becomes a constant reconciliation of the actual and the ideal in both personality and social life.

The tendency to overemphasize either the actual or the ideal is unhealthy, regardless of where it occurs, for it always involves the rejection of the other essential aspect of the whole life. Overemphasis on ideals and ultimates leads religion to reject actualities or to condemn actualities. A common example of this is an interpretation of the ideal of purity, which implies that sex is basically evil and impure. Another example is the tendency to strive for a static ideal of perfection, and responding to the inevitable failure either by an unwarranted sense of guilt or by a blind spiritual pride which refuses to accept actualities. On the practical level, parishioners frequently feel reluctant to discuss their actual problems with many clergymen because they fear the clergyman's emphasis on ideals and his scorn of the actual will lead him to condemn rather than understand them.

The ideals of religion are formulated through the use of insight symbols. The "will of God" is the symbolic form through which the ideals of Christianity find their most complete expression. But such symbols function toward the integration of personality only when they are held in close relation to actualities. There is always a strong tension be-

tween the actual and the ideal, a tension that is one distin-
guishing aspect of a religious experience. The solution of
this tension lies in the reconciliation of the actual and the
ideal in life experience. Such reconciliation is not always
achieved easily. It may require some revision of ideals or of
the interpretation of ideals or some redirection of impulses,
and either may be difficult. The reinterpretation of ideals,
for example, is more than an intellectual process; it involves
the revision of emotional attitudes. It is easy in the face of
those difficulties to succumb to the tendency to dissociate
the ideal from the actuality. This may be done by repressing
the ideal in favor of the impulse or by repressing the impulse in favor of the ideal. Either way contains the possibilities of illness, or at least of an unbalanced life, and creates
the necessity to erect some symptomatic barrier to the consciousness of guilt and anxiety.

If religion is to function in the direction of the integration of personality, the dynamic association between the symbolic ideal and the actual life experience must be maintained. Such association is not an arbitrary matter, in the
first place. It represents insight into some potentiality inherent in life, a potentiality apprehended and formulated
in symbolic terms. This apprehension is never complete,
and ideals are in constant need of criticism and revision in
the light of a greater understanding. Religious ideals become
dissociated from actualities only through a process of decay
or disintegration. In their fundamental nature, true religious
ideals are grounded in experience. They are expressive of
the way a life ought to be lived because of its inherent nature,
or the end for which personality was created. But ideals
express potentialities only when the dynamic association
between symbol and actuality is maintained. A valid ideal
is a symbolic expression of a potential but as yet unrealized
value; an invalid ideal is a symbol dissociated from reality.
It is this dynamic association between actual life processes
and potentialities and the symbolic formulation of ideals that
gives the basis for the idea that one can only move toward

a true ideal and never completely catch up with it. This is another way of apprehending the process of growth and self-realization. The function of religion is to stimulate growth, or to transform ideals into actualities. But growth enlarges our conception of our potentialities and clarifies our ideals, so that though ideals are achieved in one sense, they still remain to be achieved in another sense. And when growth ceases, the processes leading to disease and death set in. Failure to live on the basis of ideals that are inherent in human nature will inevitably lead to disease, regardless of how much this failure is bolstered by religious practice.

But ideals, like other aspects of meaning, have a way of becoming dissociated from the actual. When this occurs they become mere specific patterns of behavior, rather than goals toward which the personality may grow. They also become fixed modes of behavior by which all people of all ages in a given group tend to be judged. In this way, ideals and goals within the realm of potentiality for the adult are often forced upon a child. This can only lead to conflict and repression or to behavior contradictory to the ideal, followed by guilt. A more concrete example is the teaching of religion in regard to the ideal of love of one's fellows. Interpreted in a static sense, it would require a psychological miracle of great magnitude for many adults to accomplish this. And the same would be true of children, because their emotional development has not yet reached the stage where this is possible. Only psychological harm can come from such application of this ideal of love. On the other hand, to recognize the validity of this ideal as a goal toward which every personality may grow, and that the attainment of such a goal will be governed by such actualities as the capacity of the individual (a point at which we are not created equal) and the emotional atmosphere in which the individual lives, is to relate the ideal in a dynamically useful way to personality growth and health.[2] Religion always has been and always will be vitally concerned with the development of character through the application of ideals. In the knowledge of the growth of the emotions as discovered by dynamic psychology, religion has at its disposal some basic facts the neglect of which will hamper its effectiveness as a determinant of character.

Another result of the tendency to dissociate the ideal from the actual in religion is the development of a compulsive feature in ideals. Such dissociation places the conscious emphasis on the structure of the ideal rather than on its function. Ideals serving as a basis for healthy growth in personality need no defense—their creative functioning attests to their validity. But ideals that have become dissociated demand defense, because their very emptiness is felt. Persons living on the basis of such ideals feel an inner compulsion to force others to do likewise. The ideal thus becomes a moral precept rather than a psychological basis for growth. In group acceptance of a given symbolic structure of ideals lies security for that structure and for all who can blindly ally themselves with it, long after it has ceased to serve a dynamic function in the lives of the individuals or group concerned. When religious people feel called upon to force their ideals on others, they present a symptom of inner illness, of failure to find a dynamic integration between their ideals and the actual. True religious experience, which involves the translation of potentialities into realities, creates an inner security which makes it possible for one to be of service to others without being compulsive about it. This service is a process of sharing rather than one of forcing.

Inquiry into the genesis of the ideals of a person leads inevitably into that area where culture brings its satisfactions and pressures to bear on the growing child in order to mold its behavior in harmony with the group and to the child's response to those satisfactions and pressures. The contribution of psychoanalysis is of particular value at this point. Psychoanalysis finds conscience to be the product of two aspects of experience. In part, its development is determined by the authoritative restrictions and control exercised by the parents. This authority and the particular patterns it enforces are a reflection of the authority and patterns of the larger group.

Many parents in our culture are more concerned to have their child develop in ways that their neighbors will approve than in ways that permit the spontaneous but guided development of the child's potentialities. On the other hand, there are a few parents of rebellious temper who take strong satisfaction in raising their children to be different from the group. For the child's personality, this is just as disastrous as too much emphasis on group standards.

To the psychoanalysts, conscience is largely the "internalization of external authority."[3] This conscience, which they term the superego, operates largely below the level of consciousness. It automatically inhibits the expression of impulses through the threat of anxiety and inner punishment.

But there is another factor in the development of conscience. This is the capacity of the individual to identify himself with other people through the feelings of love. This is a process which begins early in life and is carried on into maturity. The first identifications are with the parents; the child seeks to become like them because of his affectional attachment to them. Here is a powerful source of his ideals and his conscience. Later in life he may identify himself with other people, a social cause, or with God. The acquisition of ideals through the process of identification is highly significant for religion and for religious education. It expresses the psychological truth in the statement that religion is caught, not taught.

We cannot discuss here all the psychological problems involved in the development of conscience or of the superego, and of the relation of conscience to personality development and health. We are rather concerned with the relation of conscience and ideals as they find expression in religious Weltanschauung and symbolism.

Ideals are the symbolic expression of those psychic processes which we call conscience, and are a powerful component of the individual's outlook on life. Conscience is a function of the personality that is essential to growth and self-realization. It contains some of those processes through which the individual is able to gain freedom from external control and achieve a measure of autonomy. But conscience may be warped in its development in the direction either of rigidity and overseverity or of laxity. It then functions to produce illness rather than growth and health. Religious symbols expressing ideals may serve to promote growth or to foster either of these unhealthy tendencies.

More specifically conscience and its symbolic expressions may be predominantly positive or negative in their fundamental nature and function. The negative aspects of conscience, symbolically expressed in "Thou shalt not," are the products of early childhood experiences with the authority of the home. Such a conscience functions through the use of anxiety, guilt, and the fear of punishment. It is inhibitory and rigid in character, imprisoning the personality. When negative tendencies predominate in the religious symbols of a person, it is because they dominate the life of the person. We come back to our principle, that function and structure are one. Religious persons whose symbols are predominantly negative in character spend most of their time trying not to be bad. This leads to much unhealthy frustration, unhappiness, and undesirable personality traits, such as overseverity with others and malicious gossip. Persons who spend their energy in trying not to be bad are excessively protective of the morals of others, on the one hand, and vicariously enjoy the sins of their neighbors, on the other hand. Since the aim of the negative conscience is the repression of impulses, that is, blocking their satisfaction, persons so possessed are not able to find growth, or creative happiness. Relatives of patients frequently remark: "She was such a good person. I don't understand why she should become mentally ill." Investigation always reveals a negative type of goodness in such cases, a goodness which crushed the joy out of life. There are within the church many "good people," whose static goodness is leading to illness in one form or another, rather than to an abundant life.

In a discussion of ideals and conscience bearing on negative tendencies, there is a pitfall into which many religious people fall. It involves an either-or point of view which fails to comprehend the dynamic nature of life. Either one is good, in the sense of repression, or one is bad, in the sense of expression. That free expression of infantile impulses is highly undesirable goes without saying. The individual with a lax conscience is recognized by psychiatry as a sick person, and is usually labeled as a psychopathic personality. Religion labels them by other terms, and condemns them. Between the excessive restrictions of the negative conscience and the open expression of a weak conscience lies another course, which leads to growth and health.

The negative conscience is a remnant of the authority experienced in childhood, whether this be excessive, as in the neurotic, or less exacting, as is the case in the more normal adult. Maturity of personality is achieved in part as the ghosts of childhood authority lose their control through growth. This growth takes place through other processes which also have their beginning in childhood, processes based on love rather than on fear and guilt. We have already discussed the place of love and identification in the development of conscience. It is through the elaboration of these processes that what we are calling the positive conscience is developed.

The positive conscience is symbolized in religion in terms of "Thou shalt." It thus directs the expression of impulses toward ends that are constructive. These ends are not the mere expression of impulses for the sake of personal satisfaction; they involve the expression of impulses in ways that create values for others as well as for the individual, or at least do not injure others. Growing out of the identification of the individual with the group, they become a synthesis of subjective and objective needs. Having been appropriated by the personality through love rather than fear, they bring release and freedom. Being expressed in terms that demand a positive achievement, they give expression to the conative element in personality, an expression denied by the negative ideal. They thus lead the individual out beyond himself rather than shut him up within himself. A positive conscience thus serves to strengthen the ego rather than weaken it.

The positive ideal, being an expression of a goal to be achieved, is also open to rational criticism and evaluation in a manner that is impossible for the negative ideal. Persons dominated by negative ideals are inhibited by anxiety from the exercise of their critical faculties in relation to their ideals. Their critical faculties are turned against those who do not share their ideals. The positive conscience, on the other hand, does not inhibit the intellect; it frees man's rational powers for the criticism of ideals and for the purpose of discovering adequate methods for the application of ideals to personal and social problems.

It can be seen that the negative conscience is one factor in conflict and frustration. The positive conscience, on the other hand, leads to the resolution of conflict in a creative manner. The negative conscience takes sides against the impulses, forbidding their expression. It weakens the ego in its struggle for wholeness and, therefore, operates against integration and growth. Because it is the outgrowth of the authority of childhood, the negative conscience identifies itself with the authority of the culture, and makes conscience and its symbols, religious or otherwise, the tools of the authority of the prevailing culture. Its ideals are judged on the basis of cultural standards rather than of personality values. It thus loses its power to change either persons or culture. The positive conscience, on the other hand, being the outgrowth of love relationships, becomes identified with the needs of others and finds itself in conflict with the prevailing cultural standards when those standards deny the basic needs of personality. But such a conflict does not lead to illness; it is the very soil in which personality may reach its highest development. Such persons are to be differentiated, however, from the persons who are in conflict with the culture out of a feeling of rebellion. In some externals they may bear close resemblance; in inner motivation, methods of work, and final results they are quite different.

Religion at its best directs man to positive achievements. Its symbols are a means of apprehending and formulating a positive way of life, based on relationships of love. When Jesus formulated the great Commandment in terms of love for God and for one's neighbor as oneself, he was expressing the highest ideal of which man is capable, and an ideal that leads to both integration and self-realization. But religion and religious symbols may degenerate to the level of the negative conscience and negative ideals. When this occurs, religion serves to promote neurotic and psychotic trends within the personality and within the culture.

Religion, being fundamentally a Weltanschauung that becomes formulated in a way of life, should be concerned with the whole personality in all its relationships, rather than with just a part of the total process. When religion becomes overly concerned with one aspect of life to the neglect of others, it loses its balance and fails in its vital personality function. The tendency of religion to reinforce conscience against impulses is an illustration of this. Religion at its best is just as much concerned with the impulses of love, hate, or fear as it is with the ideals that should guide their expression. Dissociation between the ideal and the impulse, the symbol and the propelling reality, is always conducive to conflict and illness. The function of religion is to make men whole, not to intensify inner struggle that can only lead to disintegration.

Religion, being concerned with making man whole, is concerned with both conscience and impulses, but also and primarily with that other aspect of personality, the conscious ego, which is the label given to those psychic processes through which man deals with both inner and external reality, and through which wholeness is achieved. These conscious processes have been traditionally expressed by religion through the use of the symbol "soul." Some years ago psychology bowed both God and the soul out of the universe. But it could not get along without an equivalent, so it used the symbol "ego," or "self." Regardless of the symbol, religion should be primarily concerned with those conscious psychic processes which function toward integration and wholeness. A positive conscience serves rather than inhibits these processes. The doctrine of the supreme value of the individual or the human soul grows out of the basic insight that no other creature is endowed with this conscious, self-directing function. But this doctrine becomes an empty symbol when theological creeds, moral codes, or institutional patterns become more important than personality values. Conscience, creeds, and cultural patterns exist for the sake of persons; persons do not exist for them. Religion as we know it today would undergo a radical change if the doctrine of the supreme value of the individual were to become a living reality rather than a dead symbol, and its contribution to the health of the community would be greatly increased.

Without apology for our symbol, we can say that a sick soul is one that is so ridden, either by impulses or a negative conscience or by a conflict between the two, that it is not free to express its potentialities and abilities creatively; and that a saved soul is one that has succeeded in organizing impulses and potentialities, with the help of a positive ideal, into a living whole that feels at home in its world. This is the psychological reality that has been expressed in the symbol of Christ as Saviour, for Christ as Saviour has been to many a positive ideal, appropriated through identification and affection rather than through authority and fear, which gives the ego power to effect and maintain a personality integration. However, as this symbol is used so frequently today, it serves lesser ends or has become altogether impotent.

Religion, at its best, serves the much-needed purpose of

strengthening the ego in its struggle for mastery. Looking at one's inner character by itself is painful, discouraging, and usually productive of anxiety. Looking at oneself in the light of a negative conscience is usually intolerable. Looking at one's inner life, or some aspect of it, in the light of what one may become is another matter. Religion does not teach men that they can pull themselves up by their own bootstraps. It teaches them that they may be lifted as they learn how to apportion their affections toward worthy ideals, or when they learn to worship that which is worthy of their worship. It also brings the insight that the struggle of the individual is the struggle of his neighbor, for it reminds him that all men have fallen short of the ideal. In the experiences of repentance and forgiveness, it offers opportunity for the reattachment of affections and for growth. Thus when religion functions properly in life, when it is a living experience rather than a mere profession or a theological formulation, it becomes a source of strength that has no equal in any other human endeavor.

The reality of religion, then, is the reality of human experience. There is no aspect of human experience that does not find expression in religious symbols. Religion functions between two worlds, the inner and the external, the actual and the ideal, the relative and the Absolute, the finite and the Infinite. It aims at the reconciliation of opposites which produces living values, and thereby seeks to counteract tendencies that lead to despair and disintegration. In the words of Whitehead: "Religion is the vision of something which stands beyond, behind, and within, the passing flux of immediate things; something which is real, yet waiting to be realized; something which is a remote possibility, yet the greatest of present facts; something that gives meaning to all that passes, and yet eludes apprehension; something whose possession is the final good, and yet is beyond all reach; something which is the ultimate ideal, and the hopeless quest."[4]

REFERENCES

1. VAN DER HOOP, J. H., *Character and the Unconscious*, p. 119. New York, 1923.
2. This is especially true of children. The emotional atmosphere of many homes blocks the healthy and religious growth of affections.
3. See ALEXANDER, FRANZ, *The Psychoanalysis of the Total Personality*, pp. 16-17. New York, 1930.
4. WHITEHEAD, A. N., *Science and the Modern World*, p. 267. New York, 1926.

CHAPTER IX

RELIGIOUS SYMBOLS IN ILLNESS AND HEALTH

A Paradox in Religious Symbolism

There is a strange paradox in symbolism, and failure to recognize it leads to grief. Man's symbols, religious or otherwise, are essential to the apprehension and understanding of reality and the expression of truth; man's symbols, religious and otherwise, are also a fruitful source of error and suffering. Clothing an idea in a religious form gives it powerful support in many minds; but an idea productive of illness is just as easily expressed in religious symbols as is an idea that leads to health. Symbolism is an essential and powerful instrument, and religion is weak today in part because it has grown inept in the use of this instrument. Only as religion learns how to use such a powerful instrument can it become a source of understanding and lead to creative living. When symbolism becomes an end in itself and religion becomes preoccupied with its symbols, it becomes the source of much error, misery, and suffering. Our problem in this chapter is this paradox in symbolism.

The consciousness of this paradox has been dim during the past few centuries. The Fundamentalist-Modernist controversy of a past generation was grounded in the failure to grasp the nature and function of religious symbols. Fundamentalists, clinging to a dead tradition, insisting on the literal interpretation of symbols, and maintaining an overemphasis on the emotional side of religion by a strangulation of the intellect, failed to see that they were slaves to symbols rather than men set free through living, growing truth. Modernists, rebelling against an outmoded and childish view of the world and of religion, and struggling for an intellectual definition that would make religion compatible with science, have largely achieved a worthy goal, but they have not developed a dynamic religion. Each group has found a great deal of error in the views of the other. The Fundamentalists have created more positive mental suffering, but the Modernists have left personality largely without the power that remakes character and culture. Neither group has given much consideration to the use of religious symbols for the purpose of grasping those realities in human experience which make men whole. They have been involved in tasks which have taken their attention all too much from the basic problems of living.

This paradox in religious symbolism grows out of a certain tendency inherent in life itself, and the bygone struggle between the Fundamentalists and Modernists was symptomatic of a deeper tension. As we have seen, life is a dynamic process which develops a structure for its own expression. The undifferentiated mass of protoplasm developing structure through the expenditure of energy arising out of response to environmental stimulation is a prototype of our problem. The functional task of religion cannot be achieved without a structure, and religious symbols constitute that structure. In all of life there is the constant tendency of structure to be overdeveloped, to become hardened, and crystallized, and to become an end in itself. The structure of religion may become fixed and hardened even as the arteries of the brain or cultural patterns.

THE USE OF RELIGIOUS SYMBOLS FOR INSIGHT OR CONCEALMENT

In their true function, religious symbols aim at providing insight into the nature and meaning of life and at formulating a way of life based on that insight. The first of these functions, that of insight or understanding, is basic, although in the actual processes of life it cannot be separated from the second. Religion has always insisted that a vision of God involves a way of life. For our purposes it is useful to discuss these two aspects separately.

It is necessary to understand the nature and aim of any reality before one can form a healthy or creative relationship to it. This is true of electricity, of sex, of personality, or of God. Insight into the nature of electricity is a problem for science; into the nature and meaning of life as a whole, a problem for religion. Religion, when it leads to truth, is always an experience of discovery. And the deeper realities of life are discovered not primarily through the reason, but through the feelings, as feelings bring to consciousness a sense of what is occurring in one's inner life. Man's sensitive feelings are a gauge through which inner equilibrium or disequilibrium is registered.

Religion has called this process of insight by the name "faith," but unfortunately that word symbolizes to many people a process which keeps the mind in the dark rather than one which brings light. Fundamental to the use of religious symbols as a means of insight is a desire or will to know. By this we mean more than intellectual curiosity; we mean also an emotional attitude bent on the discovering of answers to man's fundamental questions about life, and one which enables the individual to become aware of the significance of what is going on in his inner and external worlds.

Religious symbols, in their proper use, are always dynamic. In other words, they formulate vital processes within the experience of the individual and the group. But religious symbols always develop in a cultural tradition. As the symbolic formulation of religious faith develops in a cultural tradition, there is constant danger that more and more emphasis will be placed on the developing structure and less and less on the inner realities of experience. This danger, if not counteracted, leads to the crystallization of symbols into a fixed structure. It then becomes necessary for the believer to accept the structure and to defend it from change. The symbolic structure, originally developed as a source of

insight into life, and as an instrument of growth, now becomes an end in itself, and gathers to itself aspects of the
personality and the culture which contribute to its perpetuation. Rather than serve the purposes of growth and health,
it inhibits growth and leads to illness.

Within the very process of formulating the realities of
experience there is the danger of substituting the form for
the reality, and of developing a purely symbolic tradition.
In the days of Jesus, the Pharisees had developed religion
largely as a ceremonial tradition devoid of real meaning.
This is true also of some churches of our own day, though
others have developed it more in terms of an intellectual
tradition. In either case the dynamic relationship between
symbol and reality has been destroyed, and the symbol has
become reality. To the extent that this occurs, religion is
powerless to create new integrations within the personality
or the group. Its symbols become dead when their dynamic
relationship with inner realities is destroyed.

All this is no new insight into religion. Religious leaders
have always been aware of this danger. The Gospels record
numerous sayings of Jesus dealing with this problem. However, we are now in a position to show the relation of this
tendency to the problems of illness and health.

Religious symbols, in their proper function, are a means
through which the believer becomes aware of the nature and
aim of that with which he is confronted in his total life.
When religious symbols become overstructuralized and crystallized, they function in a way that turns the attention of
the person from the reality to the symbol. Becoming concerned with the symbol itself, the reality for which it stands
is evaded or concealed from consciousness and the symbol
becomes reality. This evasion or concealment leads to unhealthy consequences.

Becoming aware of the realities that affect one's life is by
no means easy, and there are certain obstacles in the way of
discovery. One of these is the influence of elements present
in every culture, which prefer that the individual accept

cultural patterns without seriously questioning their validity or meaning. Cultures as well as persons tend to become static, and to set up pressures to protect the status quo or powerful elements from disturbance. Another obstacle is that as children we are frequently taught or forced to justify ourselves rather than understand and accept ourselves. Another is the fact that the individual may feel too weak to handle some aspect of his personality, and is much more comfortable if he can exclude this from consciousness. Still another, and perhaps most significant obstacle, is the fact that awareness of reality often involves pain and difficulty, so that the path of least resistance, as well as freedom from pain, lies in evasion and concealment rather than in understanding. Within the personality there are tendencies directed toward the achievement of understanding and insight. But there are other tendencies driving in the opposite direction. The will to know is counteracted by a will not to know, when knowing presents difficulties which the personality does not feel capable of surmounting. Actually few individuals are able to maintain constantly the inner self-discipline required by the will to know, and most persons employ devices that serve the purpose of evasion more than they realize.

To the extent that either of these tendencies becomes structuralized in religious symbols, those symbols exert a powerful influence on the personality. An individual in an anxiety situation may gain through religious symbols a grasp of some reality which resolves the conflict in the direction of growth and brings peace. Or he may use religious symbols as an aid to the repression of the conflict or to evade the reality situation that produces anxiety. This relieves consciousness of a strain, but creates a situation in which there is a constant inner struggle such as we see in the case of Mary Jones. It requires elaboration of the repressing symbol, and sooner or later the development of some compromise and regressive solution in the form of a symptom of illness. The personality remains whole to the extent that it is able to discover the realities which threaten its existence and deal with them along constructive lines.

The direction of the personality is reflected in and strongly influenced by its use of religious symbols. When symbols remain alive, that is, when the dynamic association between symbol and reality is held intact, they lead to an ever-expanding appreciation of the nature of the individual's problem, and thus promote growth. When symbols become dead, that is, when the association is broken, they operate against growth, and when inner tension becomes too severe, toward regression. This means illness in one of its various forms. When symbols remain alive, they lead to a wholesome mastery of life; when dead, the elemental forces of life master the conscious ego, and illness results. When alive, they promote continuous integration; when dead, they become a disguise under which processes leading to disintegration operate.

The will to know or the will not to know are much more than intellectual traits. Each possesses deep emotional and conative components. It is these deeper components, such as fear, hostility, a shrinking from pain and difficulty, and other such trends, that control the intellectual processes for their own ends. Here we meet another paradox of human experience: negative feelings and strivings hold the intellect in subservience, while positive feelings and strivings release the intellect for constructive tasks. The will to know or not to know is not developed by a conscious choice of the individual so much as by the forces that struggle beneath consciousness. The fundamental task of consciousness is at the point of the focus of attention. To the extent that the conscious attention is focused on the symbol itself, and the processes of consciousness, such as reason, are involved with the symbol itself, the symbolism serves the will not to know. To the extent that attention is focused on the reality behind the symbol, and conscious thought centers in this reality, the symbolism serves the will to know. When the processes of consciousness are not strong enough to permit it to maintain its proper function of dealing with reality, deeper elements within the personality will take control. Maintaining the dynamic association between reality and its symbols by looking beyond or through the symbol to the truth it seeks to convey is, at times of severe conflict, a difficult task for the conscious ego.

Symbolism is a highly important instrument for the conscious ego. For symbols bring the meaning of experience to the level where evaluation and organization are possible. In order to do this, it is not necessary that a symbol portray or reveal the complete nature of reality at any given moment. This is obviously impossible. It is necessary, however, that there be an increasing apprehension of the nature of reality. In the process of discovering reality one never fully arrives.

Sometimes a given reality is too painful to be grasped fully, and only a gradual discovery is practicable or desirable. Again the growth of mental processes and the capacity to handle symbols and meanings plays a part. The child can grasp a symbol, the symbol "God," for example, quite as readily as can an adult. But the child cannot grasp any meaning of the symbol beyond that offered by his own limited experience and level of development. The adult should be able to find a larger meaning in a given symbol because of greater experience and development, and failure to do so may indicate a failure in development. There is a similar difference between primitive man and more highly developed man. The problems of adult life cannot be successfully solved on the basis of the comprehension of reality that is possible in childhood. Yet many adults have never succeeded in getting beyond a childish interpretation of religious symbols. For them the symbol "God" still retains its childhood significance. It may be necessary to become as a little child to enter the kingdom of God, that is, to break through adult sophistication that clouds the mind to living realities, but one cannot remain childish and remain in the kingdom of

God. The kingdom of God is the kingdom of maturing personalities.

The gradual apprehension of reality involves a characteristic of symbolism itself. A living symbol always portrays some fundamental psychological truth. Its meaning, therefore, can never fundamentally change, nor be annulled. But the apprehension of that meaning must increase if the mind is to grow. Thus the symbol "God" may stand for the central reality in life. But an individual's conception of the central reality in life and his relationship to it must change with increased experience or the symbol will serve to conceal truth. Only by maintaining the dynamic association between symbol and reality through constantly looking behind the symbol to the truth which it expresses can symbols undergo an expansion of meaning and thus promote the growth of personality.

The expanding grasp of reality that is essential to maturity and health in religion is not easy or without pain. Neither is it a purely personal experience. It requires participation in a group seeking the same ends. In this matter of growth, as in many others, the problem of the individual is also the problem of the group. It is only the exceptional individual whose personal development in religion goes beyond that of the group, and even such leaders have their roots in the best insights that the past and present of their group life accords. To this they add a personal creative element.

The religious group may serve a vital function in helping the individual become aware of the realities of his experience, either in their negative or their positive aspects. The collective symbols of religion, representing the experience of many persons, have profound value for the individual in so far as they are living symbols. Participation in the religious group, involving a strong sense of fellowship, should stimulate the individual to a discovery of the realities of his own personal experience. It should also be a source of strength and stimulation to the ego, especially at times when forces working against the discovery of reality are strong within the personality. When the symbols of the group are living and vital, they serve also as a powerful means for the development of cultural patterns on the basis of personal values.

To this end the religious group has devised certain techniques, such as corporate worship. Worship, either corporate or private, is a means of becoming aware of the reality of one's symbols, particularly the reality of God. Worship is the act of discovering what one's symbols mean. It is thus much more than an intellectual process, for that would mean only defining one's symbols. Intellectual definition and laying hold on reality through the medium of insight symbols in the mood of worship are two quite different experiences. It is the difference between philosophy and religion; the difference between "I believe" and "I know." Not all men can be philosophers, but all men can worship.

Essential as the religious group is to the developing individual, it presents a certain hazard. The paradox of symbolism holds for the group quite as much as for the individual. For the group as well as for the individual, symbols may become only empty shells of once living truth. For the group as well as for the individual, symbols become overdeveloped, crystallized, and dead. They serve the purpose of the group will not to know. Thus corporate worship itself may lose its vital function and may consist of rites in which inwardly dead men go through externally dead forms. In that case, religious symbols, far from promoting growth through an expanding comprehension of reality, serve to promote neurotic and psychotic trends both in the individual and in the culture. The religious group promotes growth within the personality and within the culture only when its symbols are alive and subject to a constant expansion of meaning in harmony with growing racial experience.

From the point of view of illness and health, the significant fact is not the particular symbol that a person uses, but the meaning of that symbol and the way in which it is used. Any religious symbol, the symbol "God," for example, may be a source of insight or a means of concealment. In talking with a certain patient on one occasion it became obvious that she was at the point of relating some experience that evidently had something to do with her illness and that gave her a strong feeling of guilt. Suddenly she dropped her head and prayed, "O God, help me to talk to this man." As her face was raised it was evident that something had happened inside, for the expression of guilt had disappeared. Looking me in the eye, she said, "God says that I do not have to talk to you." The idea of talking to me was her own in the first place, and I had asked her no questions. But talking would have brought some painful reality up to the level of consciousness. Her prayer represented a rather weak attempt to persuade herself to do something that she really did not want to do. The answer to her prayer represented a stronger element in her personality. She disguised this deeper element through her use of the symbol "God." The use of religious symbols for purposes of concealment is found just as frequently but less obviously in organized religion as in mental hospitals. In the following chapter we shall discuss more fully the problem of the expression of personality trends through religious symbols; here we are dealing with the general use of symbols.

The use of religious symbols as a means of insight may be illustrated by reference to another patient, a man of thirty who believed that he was Christ. After holding this idea for several months, he informed me that he had decided that he was not Christ after all. He went on to say that, since making this decision, he was not elated as he had been when he thought he was Christ. Indeed, he was somewhat worried, for now he would have to face certain problems. The belief that he was Christ made him feel that he had no problems, but that it was his duty to solve the world's problems. His success in seeing beneath this symbol to its significance for him led him to face the problems its use had helped him to avoid.

In religion, either inside or outside the mental hospital,

a sure symptom of the failure to keep the association between reality and symbol alive is dogmatism. Insistence on a particular intellectual definition of a religious symbol indicates that the symbol is being used as a means of concealment. Such concealment indicates a weakness in the ego, and dogmatism is a way of compensating for this weakness. Dogmatism is usually the outgrowth of an experience which resulted in the arrest of both religious and emotional development at some point in the past. It is an illustration of the crystallization of structure to the extent that the true function of religion is destroyed.

Dogmatism is not to be confused with an inner certainty that accompanies a growing religious development. Such certainty is based on the experience of some reality which has profound meaning for the individual. True religious certainty is not difficult to distinguish from dogmatism, for certainty is centered in reality, dogmatism in symbol. The difference in terms of outcome is admirably expressed in the words of St. Paul, "The letter killeth, but the spirit giveth life."[1] Emphasis on the letter, or the symbolic form, inhibits growth and creates an inner necessity to make others accept a rigid and arbitrary definition of symbols. It will lead to insistence on the use of a certain set of symbols. Life cannot be cramped into any form without serious consequences. True religious certainty will create its own forms because of its own inner motivation. For such experiences form is a minor consideration; the real emphasis is on the implications of the experience in the life of the individual and of the group. True religious certainty expresses itself in the achievement of personal and social values, rather than in the propagation of a creed. It brings to the personality a sense of security that makes possible the appreciation of the real divergence between the actual and the ideal, and a sense of humility in relation to its task. Dogmatism also brings a sense of security, but it is security in a dead form and results in a mobilizing of the individual's energy in defense of the form and away from the achievement of real values.

The security of true religious certainty stimulates the personality by directing energy toward the achievement of
values, even at the risk of danger and suffering. In other
words, it brings courage and a sense of adventure. There is
nothing more experimental in the best sense of the word than
true religious faith. True religious certainty results in a
flexibility of personality rather than in rigidity, and thus
permits new adaptations to varying internal or external circumstances. Dogmatism is not only a sign of arrested development in religion, but is also symptomatic of inner
processes which under stress may lead toward neuroses and
psychoses.

RELIGIOUS SYMBOLS AND MAN'S RELATIONSHIP TO REALITY

As we have said, insight into reality always involves
action toward reality. The vision of God always implies a
way of life. In other words, the purpose of insight is that of
establishing an appropriate relation to reality. We shall now
discuss the relationships with reality which may be developed
through symbols, religious or other, and the bearing of these
relationships on illness and health.

There are three possible relationships to any reality. There
is the relationship of escape, in which the personality seeks
to avoid some pertinent aspect of reality or to treat reality
as though it did not exist. There is the relationship of rebellion against reality, which aims at destroying it. There
is the relationship of co-operation with reality, in which there
is an endeavor to discover the nature of reality and to pattern life accordingly. It will be readily seen that these relationships will find expression in the way of life and will
lead to greatly different consequences for the personality.
Each may be formulated through the same religious symbols.

The way of escape is an immature reaction to life. It is
followed because the individual feels too weak to cope with
reality as he finds it, or to gain sufficient insight to understand it. Behind this reaction there is always a strong fear,

which leads the person to withdraw from reality as a means of self-protection. The various psychological means through which persons may close their minds to fear-producing reality are discussed fully in numerous psychological texts.[2] In a following chapter we shall discuss these in relation to religious symbols.

The way of escape, when it becomes habitual, leads to neurosis or psychosis in one form or another. In other words, this way of life is a major factor in the production of illness. Personality can be healthy only on the basis of the laws inherent in its structure. Such living is seldom easy and is never accomplished without pain and effort. To the extent that a person seeks to avoid reality, he is forced to create a pseudoreality in its place. Many symptoms of illness are such pseudorealities. They have a sense of reality to the individual because they are a substitute for some reality from which he seeks escape. To tell a person who has developed some symptom such as physical illness or delusions of persecution as forms of escape that his pains or beliefs are not real is to incur his wrath. He knows they are real, and is not able to grasp their true nature because of the function they serve in his personality. Personality is developed on the basis of inherent potentialities and laws, or it develops a false sense of reality and becomes ill.

The way of rebellion is also an immature reaction to life. It is based not so much on fear as on hate and aggression. The major drive of a person following this way of life is toward destruction. When this destructive drive is turned toward the self, the person becomes ill.[3] When it is turned directly toward the outer world, the individual becomes delinquent or criminal. In its more sublimated forms the individual becomes an enemy of society, a hater of humanity, and works out his destructiveness toward some social or cultural symbol.[4] The way of rebellion is the way of the person who has been hurt by reality and who, therefore, feels impelled to hurt in return. In this mood, individuals are usually impervious to the insight that they are really injuring themselves and that the capacity for rebellion, like that for escape, is not the way to the true joy of personality fulfillment.

The way of co-operation is the way of the mature person. As such, it is not an instinctive reaction to life; it has to be learned. Man is born not with the will to co-operate, but with the capacity to learn how to co-operate. The primary emotion expressed in co-operation is that of love. The infant can love, but not in the mature sense. Psychoanalysis has rendered a valuable service in its discovery of the basic stages of emotional development through which the capacity to love proceeds from a self-centered feeling, or self-love, to the love of the mature person who is capable of considering the interests and welfare of others on a level of equality with his own. The way of co-operation requires that the personality outgrows the egocentricity of childhood. The egocentric individual will tend to work out his relationships on the basis of either escape or rebellion. Probably no human being is able to maintain an attitude of co-operation all the time.

Co-operation is the only relationship that makes possible a healthy equilibrium between the individual organism and its environment, or between man and man, or between man and his universe. The egocentric person seeks to relate the universe, including other people, to himself. He becomes the center. Such an inverted relationship inevitably creates many tensions, as the universe is not run to suit the whims of any individual. Actually, the individual is only part of a larger Whole, and his fulfillment lies in the direction of relating himself to that larger Whole according to its laws. Man does not make the laws through which the personality achieves integration and equilibrium—he may discover those laws and co-operate with them. In so far as the individual seeks to force his will on the universe he sets in motion processes leading to his own disintegration. In so far as he seeks to relate himself to reality he sets in motion processes leading to integration, or wholeness.

The relationships of escape, rebellion, and co-operation

may be expressed through the same or through different symbols. It would be interesting and instructive to trace these fundamental relationships as they become formulated in political symbols and result in various kinds of political life. Or they might be traced in the symbols of art or philosophy. However, we shall illustrate their formulation through religious symbols.

Religious symbols are not only a means through which man grasps the nature of reality, but also a means through which he expresses his relationship to reality. It is significant that the ways of escape and rebellion both use religious symbols for the purpose of evasion or concealment of reality. Religious symbols dominated by the will to know always involve the relationship of co-operation. True insight always influences the expression and development of personality in the direction of harmony with that insight. Religion has frequently expressed this fact in terms of the will of God. In the teachings of Jesus this symbolizes the attitude of co-operation, of relating oneself to the universe rather than the universe to oneself.

But this symbol, the will of God, is also used by the individual who seeks to escape from reality. Thus a patient in the hospital quietly states that it is God's will that he is in the hospital, and that it is God's responsibility to get him out, and then sits back to wait on God's good pleasure. Needless to say, this only serves to deepen a regressive trend that is already serious, and thus makes his condition more helpless. A patient who was suffering from a physical illness, from which the physicians agreed that she should have reexpression of a desire to die, and soon developed a condition beyond the reach of the physician's medicine. Life had been hard on her, she had lost all desire to live, and the end was inevitable after she decided that she should submit to "the covered, resigned herself to "the will of God" as a symbolic will of God," which was, as she saw it, to die. Strangely enough, the ministrations of an inadequately trained clergyman assisted the process. Mary Jones insisted that God work out her problems on the basis of her own conception of right and wrong, and of the nature of love. God was to solve the problem according to her ideas. Many other illustrations could be given.

The symbols of religion may also be used to express the way of rebellion. Sometimes this is done by denying the truth or value of religion or of the church. There is a marked difference between the individual who realizes the weakness of religion or of the church, and the person who is motivated by a deep feeling of "being against" the church or something which it represents. Thus an individual may reject the symbol "God" with a great deal of feeling because to him the symbol stands for something, perhaps the authority of his father, against which he is inwardly but unconsciously struggling. The feeling of rebellion, regardless of the object toward which it is expressed, always carries with it a profound ego value—the person feels great satisfaction and assurance in his courage to fight against something. In children this is frequently interpreted as a mark of equality with the adult. Many adults likewise regard their ability to discard religion or to rebel against religious symbols as a sign that they are mature and as a proof that religion, after all, is childish. They are unable to see that their own view of religion is childish or to see through their rebellious mood to its significance for their personality. The mood of rebellion, as expressed against and through symbols of religion, is more the mood of the child seeking freedom from authority than of the mature person seeking to discover realities worthy of his co-operation. It should be recognized, on the other hand, that institutional religion has frequently presented its symbols in a way that implied a meaning that would inspire rebellion rather than create a co-operative allegiance.

The rebellious attitude may be expressed also in an espousal of religious symbols, rather than rejection of them. Sometimes this is done by using religious symbols to bolster a rebellious attitude toward symbols from another area of life. The refusal of the group known as Jehovah's Witnesses to salute the flag on the ground of a superior allegiance to God expresses this attitude. The Fundamentalist-Modernist controversy provided a rich cultural opportunity for the symbolic expression of hostility and rebellion on the part of adherents of each view. For a Christian minister to say from his pulpit that Christians should tolerate Jews but not associate with them is an expression of rebellion against the Christian teaching of the brotherhood of man through the use of the very symbols whose true meaning he was decrying.

Another way in which religious symbols may be used to express the attitude of rebellion is through identifying them with the values of culture. This likewise represents the subtle expression of deep emotional needs. When the real values of religion conflict with the values idealized by culture, some adjustment is required. This adjustment may be made in one of three ways. The values of religion and the use of religious symbols may be completely denied, and other values, such as profits, success, or social prestige, and their symbols may be made central in the life of the individual or the group. This does not mean that such persons cease to worship; it merely defines the object of their worship. Or, religious values and their symbols may be accepted by the individual, and the values and symbols idealized by culture may be given a subordinate place or even rejected. This is a difficult adjustment, requiring strong identification with religious values and uncommon strength of personality.

The third adjustment lies midway between these two. It consists in adopting the symbols of religion, but redefining them in a manner harmonious with the values of culture. The emotional conflict is thus solved by continued allegiance to the instrumental values of culture, on the one hand, supported by symbols taken over from religion, on the other hand. Thus religion becomes closely identified with the status quo. Attendance at church becomes a symbol of social respectability, or that one is a reliable businessman, rather than a means of re-evaluating one's life in the light of the Christian teaching of love of one's neighbor. God becomes a sort of cosmic Businessman, whose will becomes identified with the needs of a capitalistic culture. Or he becomes a cosmic Politician, whose will is identified with the demands of political expediency. Or he becomes a benevolent old gentleman who will richly reward those of his children who do what is "right," and what is right is determined by what the culture says is right, regardless of the fact that culture today is confused at this point. But the sanctification of culture through the appropriation of religious symbols does not change the realities of the situation. The same psychological principle is involved in the masking of fascist trends by the use of the symbols of democracy.

The attitude of rebellion may find expression by redefining religious symbols in terms of the more immediate and instrumental goals of culture, and this may have serious consequences for both personality and religion. It creates a make-believe existence in which psychological processes that are unhealthy are masked by symbols that are accepted as portraying a sound way of life. It produces a false sense of security, as the individual is never quite sure of his goals. It places the person on the defensive, for to have the validity of either his actual goals or his symbolic expression questioned is to intensify the conflict.

To condemn from the pulpit this use of religious symbols is to miss the point. It is not something that can be changed by condemnation. And condemnatory pulpit utterances are themselves so frequently based on a feeling of rebellion that it becomes only a situation where poison is being combated with more poison. To discuss the psychological effects of the frustrations which are part of the professional and personal life of clergymen is beside the point here, but it can be mentioned that one result of such frustration is the tendency to rebel against the frustration through the form of pulpit utterances of a condemnatory nature. This is not done deliberately, but is an expression of the same tendency to confuse symbols and reality.

What this means is that to be healthy one must be genuine, and this in turn means the use of symbols that honestly express one's meaning and the refusal to use symbols as a disguise or an empty form. Symbols that are not genuinely used do not promote growth or integration of personality, and in a time of crisis offer no strength to the personality.

Before ending this discussion of the way of rebellion, something needs to be said to clarify its value in certain situations. Our culture, including religion, looks upon rebellion in most of its forms as something to be punished. To this end, officials are maintained to punish criminals and social pressures are developed against persons whose views or behavior diverge from those generally accepted. But rebellion may actually be an attempt on the part of a person to throw off some form of external domination and grow up. In numerous situations, especially in children and youth, it represents a fighting reaction against unjust or unreasonable demands from the environment. At such times the child has but two alternatives. He may submit to external domination and suffer a severe crippling of his personality. Or he may fight against it and seek to free himself from it. The healthy growth of personality sometimes requires rebellion against intolerable parental domination as the first step toward self-direction. Culture and even religion often approve such domination under the disguise of the symbol of "honor to father and mother." But such domination may result in the permanent crippling of personality. The religious worker will find occasions when he can assist persons only by helping them to fight against some situation which threatens to crush them. But if he is skillful, he will not stop here. He will try to lead the individual to understand the nature and reason for his rebellion as well as the fact that rebellion is powerless to develop his personality in a positive way. The best it can do is to free the person from unjust or intolerable conditions. When through mismanagement of a specific reaction to a specific situation, rebellion becomes a deep-seated or permanent reaction to life in general, it becomes unhealthy. The task of religion is to lead persons through rebellion to the relationship of co-operation. Religion, however, frequently treats the rebellious person as does the law. This has been admirably described by Plant when he says: "Truancy, for example, is often the first sensible act in a situation involving the forcing of a child through an impossible school situation. The forces of law and order punish truancy with the same solemn insistence that they would put ice on the thermometer to assure themselves that the day was not uncomfortably hot." [5]

In the teaching of Jesus the central law of life was expressed in terms of a love of God involving the whole personality. God symbolized a Reality that was very personal, yet beyond the personal; a Reality that was universal and permanent, yet immediate; a Reality that was ever creative, and a Reality that could be known only through co-operative faith. It is through such a Reality that religion seeks to overcome man's egocentricity. Life becomes centered in the object it worships. It is through the act of worship which involves the directing of one's affections on such a Reality that religion at its best seeks to overcome man's egocentricity and develop a co-operative attitude.

But egocentricity may be readily expressed and strengthened through religious symbols. This involves the attempt to force one's ego on the world, an inflation of one's ego to cosmic proportions. We see this in the patient who says, "I am Christ." Such exaggerated indentification occurs when the ego is under very severe stress and its very existence seems threatened internally. Another illustration of egocentricity raised to cosmic proportions is found in a patient who said, "I am the Pivotal Point of the Universe." She then proceeded to organize the universe around herself as the center. This is obviously the idea of a sick personality, unable to love the world or anything in it and, therefore, forced to direct all of her love to herself. The human personality is so constructed that it must love, and only as it succeeds in directing a large portion of its affections to something outside itself can it escape the dangers of self-love. Being the "Pivotal Point of the Universe" is an expression of the tendency to relate the universe to oneself in a way designed to eliminate all harsh and unpleasant reality.

But the mental hospital is not the only place where one finds religious symbols perverted from their real purpose, and used to express an egocentric relationship to one's world. Here is one of the great dangers of the ministry. By virtue of the clergyman's position and function, egocentric individuals may be strongly moved to enter it. This is not to say that all clergymen enter the profession from this motive; it is merely to point out what happens in some cases. The symbol of service to humanity has a strong appeal to egocentric individuals, within either the church or social organizations, service clubs or business enterprises. The symbol of service to humanity is an acceptable cloak for egocentricity. Again, the tendency in religion to identify a given creed or theology with the absolute truth, or accepting membership in a given group as a guarantee that one is among God's chosen, is also an expression of egocentricity.

Egocentricity is an essential characteristic of a competitive culture. The slogan, "Every man for himself," breeds the attitude of love of self and hostility toward those who get in one's way. It is not, therefore, to be wondered at that so much religion today is essentially egocentric, for religion today, far from exerting its essential function as a critique and changer of culture in the direction of personality values, is itself largely dominated by a competitive culture. Competition among the churches is symptomatic of this domination. It is a way of distracting attention from its incongruous relationship with the culture. Religion, therefore, finds itself facing the difficult task of creating co-operative personalities in a highly competitive culture and with the meaning of its own symbols confused with cultural values. The problem is made more severe by the fact that the forces making for competition have learned to use the symbols of religion for the purpose of masking the real nature of their motivation, both to themselves and to the church. And the church, being more concerned with the formal and intellectual aspects of symbolism and having become crystallized in the form of an institution economically dependent on the culture, has been blind to the emotional and dynamic aspects of its symbolism in both the individual and culture. Thus the very symbols of co-operation—love for God, love for one's fellows, the Golden Rule, and others—have been perverted into symbols masking the spirit of competition and are used to disguise the real meaning of our dominant cultural trends. At the same time they serve as a bulwark for that culture. Thus, in the words of Jesus, "wisdom is vindicated by all her children." [6]

To the extent that a person is egocentric he is in danger of being hurt by others or by life itself. The egocentric individual greatly magnifies the usual frustrations of life and tends to exaggerate small pains. There is, therefore, the constant tendency to build up defenses designed to protect the ego. One of these defenses is the utilization of suffering, however small, as a means of getting attention and sympathy from others. The neurotic person does this to a marked degree. Another is the feeling of being a martyr; amplified, this becomes a feeling of being persecuted. Another is the inflation of the ego to the point where it seems impervious to injury, but actually is very susceptible. All these, and other defenses, lead in only one direction, that of illness. In other words, to the extent that a person is egocentric he is in danger of becoming ill in an attempt to protect himself from inevitable psychological suffering. One fundamental task of religion is that of helping men to overcome their egocentricity.

Any experience involving a crisis for the ego has in it not only the seeds of illness, but also those of health. The crisis may be met in either way, except that in some persons the degree of egocentricity and the severity of the suffering combine to make a healthy solution almost, if not entirely, impossible. It is well known that many people turn to religion at a time of crisis. Whether religion functions in the direction of illness or of health at such times depends on the meaning of its symbols and how they are used. We have said above that religion at its best strengthens the ego. But its true strengthening does not come by building artificial defenses. This comes by promoting its development and by helping it to deal realistically with forces that threaten it. The use of religion to strengthen an oversevere conscience in its battle with inner impulses only serves to weaken the ego. This is clearly illustrated in the experience of Mary Jones. The use of religion to bring an understanding of the nature of the forces in conflict and for the discovery of a solution that will lead to a true satisfaction of inner needs will strengthen the ego. But the healthy satisfaction of inner needs does not come from the ego itself; it comes from some aspect of the "other-than-I," something outside the ego. And it comes only through the development of an harmonious or co-operative relationship with external reality—by learning to love something other than oneself. It is true that many persons feel strong only when they are working against or competing with other people. But this is a false sense of strength, based on hostility created as a reaction to an injury, not on love. Religion at its best aids in promoting the development of the ego by leading the individual to direct his affections to realities outside and beyond himself.

One of the deepest needs of personality, the need for a sense of union or unity with others, can be satisfied only on the level of a co-operative relationship. To the extent that an individual is egocentric and a culture is competitive this need is frustrated in the central activities of life. On the individual level, egocentricity leads to the building up of symbols which give one a sense of status in relation with others. Thus an address on a certain street, the make and year of car one drives, the amount of income one makes, the social circle in which one moves, and many other externals become symbols through which the individual defines his relationship with others. The danger of such symbols in centering the personality in unreality should be evident. For persons who can achieve what the culture accepts as symbols of worth and status, the danger is in the direction of ego inflation. For persons who cannot achieve this, the danger is in terms of ego deflation, resulting in a chronic feeling of frustration and inferiority and, in turn, resentment, either concealed or expressed. On the group level, a sense of union is frequently achieved through the opposition of one group to another. In a competitive culture unity is frequently achieved through mobilizing resentment and hatred against what is considered to be a common enemy. But this does not give sound satisfaction for the need for unity. One cannot be a member of a group unified by hatred without becoming suspicious of one's colleagues. Unity on any basis other than a true willingness to co-operate is in the end self-defeating. Withdrawal or isolation involves a complete frustration of the need for union with others and always leads to illness either in the personality or in cultural groups.

The tendency to find membership in a group on the basis of external symbols which are necessary adjuncts of a competitive culture is definitely unhealthy, as it leads to a false sense of satisfaction and gives no reality capable of integrating the personality in a time of crisis. The symbols which give status in a competitive culture are likely to be swept away overnight by forces operating within that very culture. Furthermore, one is forced to spend his energy in safeguarding those symbols, even though it means a sacrifice of deeper personal values. Thus many men have sacrificed their families, their characters, their health, in order to safeguard their bank account. The inner tensions created by this situation and the failure of personality to find wholesome satisfactions in the daily business of living are together an immediate factor in many personality breakdowns, particularly in middle life and after. It should not be surprising, therefore, to find patients entering a mental hospital who point to some symbol of culture to prove either that they are not sick or that they are worthy to be put to death for their sins. Thus a woman points to her "business" and her "property" as proof that she cannot possibly be ill, when investigation shows that there is little reality in either of these symbols and that she is actually quite ill. A man points to financial reverses as a sign that he is a great sinner and worthy of death. That there are deep psychological factors in these illnesses is not to be denied. What we are saying is that the person's attempt to find an integration and sense of union with a group on the basis of these symbols has failed for both psychological and cultural reasons. A breakdown in personality is always a breakdown in culture, in spite of the superior attitude which our culture takes toward individuals who cannot retain their balance.

The way of escape offers a false sense of unity with external reality through symbols of dependence or through manifestly erotic symbols that create a passing ecstatic experience. It ultimately leads to isolation in some form of illness. The way of rebellion in exceptional cases completely severs one from his world, but frequently individuals with such feelings find a unity with like-minded persons against a common cause.[7] In a competitive culture symbols of achievement become a powerful but uncertain source of unity or status.

The only basis of a sense of unity capable of producing healthy and growing personalities is co-operation, when this is taken to mean the discovery of the nature and function of life and the endeavor to relate oneself to that discovery. Such an attitude gives a sense of union that creates wholeness of personality because it provides a basis on which the individual can work together with some reality in terms of the natural universe or some social group toward a worthy goal. The scientist, unifying himself with some aspect of nature by working in harmony with its laws, is an illustration of this principle. However, a man may be able to reconcile himself to natural law but not to the laws and values by which personality is developed and integrated. For the latter involves deeper dynamic aspects of personality which may be temporarily repressed in the scientific laboratory. Working together with other people toward personal or social values is an art that is difficult to learn because it involves outgrowing egocentricity. The idealization of co-operation by a competitive culture should not be accepted as an adequate illustration of this principle of unity. For in a competitive culture co-operation is frequently more of a symbol of concealment than a reality of life, it is used in subservience to the ends of competition, and is frequently used to compensate for some of the evils of a competitive system. The co-operative way of life provides a healthy sense of union with others only to the extent that it is the expression of genuine feelings within the individual.

One of the chief Christian symbols of real unity with one's fellows is that of brotherhood. Under this symbol the Christian religion expresses an ideal in which the status of an individual in the group depends basically on his being a person, rather than on some other symbol, such as money or other acquisition. This symbol stands for an ideal that may become a reality only at the price of infantile and childish self-love. Within a competitive culture there are always forces at work seeking to destroy the validity of this ideal, for its achievement would transform a competitive culture. One way of destroying its validity is by pointing out that it is impracticable, which usually is a concealed admission that it is difficult and that it conflicts with other values more highly cherished. Another way is to redefine the symbol in terms of lesser realities, and thus confuse all concerned. A certain kind of brotherhood is of practical use even in a culture devoted to material values. But this does not provide the deeper sense of unity which personality seeks.

The way of co-operation has to be learned. The individual, in infancy, is utterly dependent on his environment and at the mercy of his own impulses. The processes of thought, through which the necessary understanding is achieved, are not yet developed. In other words, the infant is not free to co-operate. This freedom has to be achieved as the person grows into maturity.

But such freedom is not a matter of asserting oneself against the environment. This is the error of a one-sided individualism, which fails to see personality in its true setting. Personality does not exist apart from its larger environment, and it is this environment in part that one must learn to co-operate with.

Freedom to co-operate is developed as one discovers and accepts those areas of life in which he can achieve autonomy, and those areas in which he is not and cannot be self-governing.[8] But autonomy never means a disregard for law; it means self-direction in accordance with law. Thus freedom always involves responsibility, and the person who cannot accept responsibility for himself and for dealing with whatever he finds within himself is likely to forfeit his freedom in terms of either the restraint of an illness or the external restraint imposed by culture. The same is true of the person who cannot accept authority in its proper sphere and degree. There is in many persons a tendency to rebel against external authority because they have not found emancipation from the frustrations of excessive parental authority in childhood. Freedom is possible only for the purpose of co-operation, never for that of escape or rebellion. Co-operation, on the other hand, is the only way to freedom, for only through co-operation does personality become liberated through the achievement of those higher values without which life tends to lose its meaning.

Traditional religion has been much concerned with the problem of freedom, but largely in terms of the doctrine of the freedom of the will. The truth of this doctrine has been asserted and reasserted against the scientific doctrine of determinism. This has been part of an intense belief on the part of religious leaders that they had to defend religion against science and scientific doctrines. It is a sad commentary that during these very years when there has been so much assertion of the freedom of the will mankind has been gradually enslaved by economic, political, and military movements. The true function of religion is not to engage with science in intellectual discussions; it is, rather, teaching men how they may achieve freedom. Freedom consists in developing the organism's capacity for initiative and spontaneity, not on the basis of impulses, but on the conscious recognition of realities and of the consequences of various relationships to those realities. It also involves reconciliation with those external realities which play a determining role within the personality. Again we are faced with the problem of the reconciliation of opposites, and the paradox that personality is in part determined and yet has the capacity for a limited degree of freedom. As a theologian has written: "Our physical and mental constitution and our social and material environment map out for us the main lines of our activity, and only to a limited degree are we able to modify and direct them. Our conduct is far more dependent on hidden forces of our own being and of the surrounding world than most of us realize; and so intimate and subtle is this dependence that no finite mind is in a position to determine the exact extent of our freedom and responsibility."[9]

Within its own symbols, religion has expressed these fundamental realities, stressing at times the one and then the other. The Calvinistic doctrine of predestination is as thorough an expression of determinism as science ever developed. The Christian symbol, the will of God, expresses the idea of a reality that is inexorable, but in vital religion this has always been balanced by other symbols implying the capacity of man to accept or reject that will, accompanied by a recognition of the consequences of either choice. Religion has at its disposal powerful techniques such as worship, preaching, religious education, individual guidance, and the development of the religious fellowship, through which its function of helping man gain freedom for co-operation is achieved. But these techniques are sadly in need of development and revision in the light of modern knowledge of man and society, and for the alleviation of the spiritual problem of modern man.

The Need of Balance in Religious Symbolism

The use of religious symbols for the purposes of understanding and co-operation involves certain other problems requiring some discussion. One of these is the need of balance in the content of religious symbols. We have already referred to the dangers involved in an overintellectualization of religion. This is one example of a lack of balance. For religion to promote health its symbols must maintain conscious meaning on the intellectual, emotional, and conative levels simultaneously. An overemphasis on the intellectual side develops a rationalistic formulation that is cold, and impotent to integrate personality because it represses feeling and striving. An overemphasis on the emotional side leads to immaturity in thought and behavior, to ideas and activities that offer expression of feeling without the guidance of reason and the achievement of real values. An overemphasis on the conative side of personality leads to fanaticism, to activity of an irrational sort, and in its milder forms, to an absorption with the symbol of service without any rational conception of what service means. Overemphasis on any of these aspects means that the motivation is more on the unconscious level than the conscious, and that religion is not fulfilling its functions of bringing insight and understanding. Such religion, if not extreme, may yield some social values, but always at the expense of personality values.

One of the practical results of overemphasis on one aspect of personality is a splitting within the personality itself. One sees this illustrated in the more liberal theological schools, where it presents a mental health hazard of major importance of which, except in rare instances, both faculty and students are unaware. Students frequently enter such schools from a more conservative background, and motivated by a religion that they learned in childhood. They immediately find a wide divergence between the ideas expressed in the classroom and the emotional attitudes motivating their personal lives. Some students never become aware of this conflict, but find themselves losing interest in their classes (a situation that is easily rationalized!). Others openly rebel against the doctrines taught, and work out a great deal of hostility against the professors. Others repress the conflict by developing an unusually strong enthusiasm for the new ideas. Some students become conscious of the problem but make an unhealthy solution. The writer witnessed an argument between a group of theological students in one of our liberal schools within the past year. The argument was between students representing the liberal intellectual point of view and the more conservative point of view. Interestingly enough, it was carried out by the use of highly significant symbols. The problem, in the words of the students, was this. "If the heart said, Believe this, and the head said, Believe that, which should we believe?" The conservative students all agreed that in a case of the heart against the head they would follow their hearts and reject their heads. The liberal students all agreed that in such a case they would reject their hearts and hold fast to their heads. Neither group saw that each solution involved an unhealthy splitting of personality, and that they were not fit to preach to others until they had found a religious faith capable of making them whole, of integrating heart, head, and life energy. Many theological students have entered a sacrificial but uncreative ministry because their hearts pulled them one way, their heads another, and their energy was consumed by the conflict, and was not free for the work to which they were giving their lives.

Another kind of balance that must be maintained is one between interpretation and fact. The Weltanschauung of religion does not exclude facts; it involves the interpretation of facts in terms of their meaning for human life. The crystallizing process in life tends to freeze the Weltanschauung on a given level of factual knowledge and, therefore, to resist the inclusion of new facts. This is the psychological basis of the conflict of religion with science. Science is constantly discovering new facts. These facts are part of the universe, the meaning of which religion must interpret. For religion to teach a Weltanschauung compatible with the factual knowledge available before the rise of science is to cramp the emotional and intellectual development of personality and create a basis for illness. For religion to create a healthy way of life it must eagerly and actively include in its Weltanschauung all newly discovered facts. In other words, it must grow with the growing experience of the race. Religious symbols incapable of expansion of meaning should give way to new symbols expressing the truth as man today sees it. Furthermore, religion is concerned with certain values, the significance of which is amplified rather than abrogated by the discovery of new facts. Thus facts gathered today in both psychology and sociology attest to the necessity of the religious principle of love as a central necessity of life, and they offer a basis on which the application of this age-old principle can be made more intelligently and with enlarged significance. To be able to revise the meaning of religious symbols and to develop new symbols through the acquisition of knowledge from other disciplines is a sign of health.

REVERSIBLE AND IRREVERSIBLE RELIGIOUS STRUCTURE

In the first section of this book, reference was made to the concepts of reversible and irreversible structure. A physiological illustration of this is a blood vessel that is constricted by emotional tension. In the early stages of this condition, and for a period of time, the release of the emotional tension permits the blood vessel to return to its normal functioning. However, prolonged constriction under emotional tension creates physiological changes within the blood vessel. Release of emotional tension will not alter this changed physiological structure. It has become fixed and irreversible.

In this section we have been discussing the structuralization of meaning through religious symbols, and in this chap-

ter we have pointed to the strong tendency for this structure
to change from a fluid form of expression to a crystallized
form, which stifles expression. In other words, there is a
point at which religious structure becomes fixed and irreversible. This is a danger point for personality and for the religious group.

Personality maintains its health as the meaning of life
expands with growing experience. This necessitates the constant revision of the meaning of religious symbols and the
development of new symbols when the need arises. It also
necessitates the use of religious symbols to stimulate growth
when inertia or conflict within the personality or the culture
tends to block growth. Thus health depends on a certain stability of the symbolic structure in order to support the personality, on the one hand, and on a flexibility of the structure
in order that growth may take place, on the other. When,
under the stress of internal or external conflict and frustrations, the flexibility of the structure is not maintained, and
it becomes rigid, personality also suffers, but more insid-
iously. Religious structure, like social or physiological structure, may be crystallized to the point where it is irreversible.
Then it ceases to perform its true function in personality
and promotes illness.

Irreversible religious structure is a problem not only for
the individual; it is one for the religious group as well. In
a sense it is more serious in the religious group, for through
group pressure it may adversely influence the lives of many
individuals. Stability balanced by flexibility is as essential in
group structure as in individual symbols. Speaking of the
structure of society, Whitehead writes: "The art of free society consists first in the maintenance of the symbolic code;
and secondly, in fearlessness of revision, to secure that the
code serves those purposes which satisfy enlightened reason.
Those societies which cannot combine reverence to their
symbols with freedom of revision, must ultimately decay
either from anarchy, or from the slow atrophy of life stifled
by useless shadows."[10] The refusal or inability of institu-

tional religion to revise its symbolic structure is responsible for many of the attacks that have been made against it, as well as for the lifelessness of many people who are seeking salvation in dead institutional forms. This problem may have been in the mind of Jesus when he insisted that new wine should not be put in old bottles.

In the mental hospital as well as out of it are to be found many persons suffering from a "slow atrophy of life stifled by useless shadows." These shadows are the reflections of past experiences with which they have not come to terms. And these shadows frequently find expression in religious symbols. The case of Mary Jones illustrates the development of rigidity in religious structure in a way that imprisons personality. Many persons assume that because an illness has been structuralized in religious forms it is, therefore, easy to cure by religious techniques. The reverse is true. Persons whose illness is expressed in religious forms may be the most difficult to cure. If a religious delusional system, for example, is violently destroyed, the individual either goes to pieces completely or rebuilds a more psychotic system in defense. To change that system constructively would amount to undoing long years of faulty living, the results of which are concealed in the system. Religious symbols are indeed a stimulus to growth when properly used, but once a person has secured a regressive trend under the guise of religious symbols he is no longer susceptible to such stimulation. He is bound to maintain his system at any cost.

In many religious circles there is a sickly sentimental belief in the power of religion to change any personality. But in its more realistic moments religion has had the insight that a life may reach a point beyond which there is no turning back. The Hebrew prophet cautioned his people: "Seek ye the Lord while he may be found, call ye upon him while he is near." [11] And Jesus spoke about the unpardonable sin, a doctrine that has caused no end of intellectual difficulty because its significance in life has been missed. Behind each of these sayings lies the truth that, while the curative forces of life may be constantly available, there comes a time when the structure of individual life is so fixed that these forces are rendered impotent. Freedom to co-operate is maintained only as religious symbols undergo constant revision in the light of the whole of man's growing experience.

Religion is man's attempt to discover the nature and meaning of life and to formulate a way of life based on that discovery. Symbols are the tools available for that purpose. But symbols are also a source of error, depending on the nature of dynamic forces within personality and within the process of symbolization itself. In discharging its function religion has had to deal with the problem of right and wrong, the problem of man's relation to his fellow men, and the problem of ultimate truth and man's relationship to it. It is a fundamental assumption of Christianity that this Reality has in a unique manner been discovered by or revealed in Christ. In the tremendous social cataclysm that rocks civilization today there is a laboratory, created at a tremendous cost, in which men capable of insight may discover the errors in their way of life. In our hospitals, both mental and general, there is another laboratory, also created at tremendous cost, in which men capable of insight may learn similar lessons. But these are negative results. Religion is called upon to discover anew the meaning of life, to embody that meaning in symbols that may be intelligible and powerful to modern man, and to develop techniques capable of transforming personality and of leading men out of the night and into the day.

REFERENCES

1. II Corinthians 3:6.
2. HORNEY, K., *The Neurotic Personality of Our Time*. New York, 1937.
   BROWN, J. F., *The Psychodynamics of Abnormal Behavior*. New York, 1940.
   MENNINGER, KARL A., *The Human Mind*. New York, 1937.
3. MENNINGER, KARL A., *Man Against Himself*. New York, 1938.

4. See VALTIN, JAN, *Out of the Night*. New York, 1941.
5. PLANT, JAMES, *Personality and the Cultural Pattern*, p. 313. New York, 1937.
6. Luke 7:35. Moffatt's translation.
7. MENNINGER, KARL A., *Man Against Himself*, pp. 204-207. New York, 1938.
8. For an illuminating, but technical discussion of the problem of autonomy and heteronomy, and of the need of the individual for integration with superindividual wholes or values, see ANGYAL, ANDRAS, *Foundations for a Science of Personality*, especially chaps. 2, 4, 6, and 8. New York, 1941.
9. KNUDSON, A. C., *The Doctrine of Redemption*, p. 160. New York, 1933.
10. WHITEHEAD, A. N., *Symbolism, Its Meaning and Effect*, p. 88. Princeton, 1927.
11. Isaiah 55:6.

CHAPTER X

RELIGIOUS SYMBOLS AND SOME ASPECTS OF PERSONALITY

THUS far we have discussed broad, general trends in personality as they are expressed through religious symbols. Some specific elements of personality also have been discussed, but only as they illustrate some aspect of these broader trends. In this chapter, we shall discuss more specific trends, seeking to distinguish further between the healthy and the pathological in religious expression.

Two difficulties become apparent at the outset of such a discussion. One is the comparatively small amount of study that has been done in this field from any point of view other than the psychoanalytic. The psychoanalytic contribution is valuable and we shall draw on it rather heavily. But there is a great need today to study this problem from the point of view of religious symbolism itself. Such a study must be carried on by properly trained clergymen working in numerous parishes. It is here that the actual processes leading to either illness or health show themselves early in both religious and cultural patterns, and it is here that they need to be studied, understood, and properly handled. In hospitals and prisons we see the end results of these processes in exaggerated forms, and from a study of the grossly pathological much can be learned about health. Research in each field is essential. However, far more work has been done on the definitely pathological side than on the more normal side. But as long as clergymen are largely held to the role of promoters of institutions, and religious symbols are utilized for institutional rather than personality values, little constructive work can be done on the problems we are discussing.

A second difficulty lies at the point of interpretation of religious symbols. Some persons have so intellectualized the meaning of religious symbols, and have defined them so completely in so-called "objective" terms, that any suggestion that they portray a subjective or psychological truth will be immediately rejected. Others, having become vaguely familiar with the Freudian concept of symbols and the Freudian emphasis on the sexual content of symbols, will confuse our concept with the Freudian and will reject the one because they reject the other. Still others, looking for short cuts, will assume that, because a certain religious symbol has a particular meaning to one person, it therefore has the same meaning to all persons who use it. But this is not true. A religious symbol may have different meanings to one individual and may express several meanings simultaneously. To posit a fixed meaning for a religious symbol is to reveal a complete lack of understanding of the problem. And to read into a religious symbol a meaning that is not there is another danger.

But the difficulties involved in the interpretation of religious symbols are no excuse for avoiding the problem. Health lies in the direction of facing and understanding the problem, and in learning how to develop and use a medium of high potential value to man. To discover the pathological use of religious symbols is just as important as to discover their healthy use, and certainly more desirable than being blind to the problem. Indeed, it can be said that one cannot fully understand the healthy use of religious symbols without some understanding of the pathological use, for these are but two sides of the same human problem.

Through religion and religious symbols many dynamic elements in the personality may find expression. We shall discuss this problem first in terms of certain aspects of personality and then in terms of certain dynamisms of adjustment.

THE EXPRESSION OF LOVE THROUGH RELIGIOUS SYMBOLS

An aspect of personality that finds particular validity in religion is love. But love is of different kinds, and each of

these may find expression in religion. We have already discussed the love of the young child, which is characterized by
strong dependence and lack of responsibility, and its expression in religion. Another kind of love that finds expression in religion is masochism. Masochism is a kind of love in
which one receives pleasure through pain and suffering. This
pleasure may be experienced as frankly sexual, or as emotional without any conscious sexual aspect. There are many
ways, besides physical suffering, in which a person may injure
himself. Thus a young man forgets an appointment with a
prospective employer and thereby forfeits his chance for a
position which he desires very much. Such persons may become experts in unconsciously arranging situations that inevitably lead to hurt feelings, or to the denial of legitimate
ambitions.

Suffering has always been a problem for religion, as we
have indicated in previous chapters. A masochistic individual, therefore, finds in religious symbols and ideas a fruitful
field for exploitation along the line of his unconscious but
dominant interest. Religion has always had its martyrs, and
martyrdom is particularly attractive to the masochistic individual. The masochistic person will easily accept an interpretation of religion that makes life unnecessarily hard and takes
all the joy out of it—except the joy of suffering. Another
form of masochism in religion is an overemphasis on the
sufferings of Christ, on the idea of "carrying one's cross,"
or on the suffering of God. By overemphasis we mean placing
these aspects of religion in a position of central importance
without balancing them with symbols portraying other aspects of experience. This overemphasis is made for a purpose, of which the person is not aware—that of gaining satisfaction through the contemplation of symbols expressing the
idea of suffering. Suffering as such is unconsciously a great
value to the masochistic individual, and religious symbols
may be and are used for this purpose.

There are some individuals of adult years in whom there is
such a strong masochistic trend that they are neurotic be-

cause of it. Such individuals may find a structuralization of their masochistic way of life in religious symbols expressing the idea of suffering. They will be impervious to symbols expressing other aspects of experience. Some persons of this kind may find sufficient outlet for their masochistic trends in religion to enable them to maintain a position of respect in the community. The danger comes when masochistic persons gain positions of leadership in the church, and through their emotional fervor focused on symbols of suffering influence others in the same direction. There is in every human being a capacity for masochism, and it is especially dangerous for the growing personality to come under the influence of a person or group whose religious symbols are predominantly of this type. When religion leads to self-depreciation, to over-emphasis on guilt or punishment, or to the acceptance of sacrifice and suffering as an end in itself, it contains a strong masochistic element and has in it the seeds of mental illness, on the one hand, or of self-destruction, on the other. Such religion will present to the growing personality the alternatives of rejection as one-sided or of acceptance involving a crippling of the personality through the elaboration of the masochistic trend.

Religion at its best has always included a large element of sacrifice. But religion at its best has never accepted sacrifice, or suffering, as an end in itself; it has always been a means of achieving some greater end. Sacrifices made in order to gain some socially useful goal or because of a value (other than that of pleasure) worthy of some sacrifice for its achievement are constructive for the personality and contribute to growth. But vicarious pleasure in the sacrifice of Christ may be nothing more than emotional intoxication achieved through the symbolic stimulation of a masochistic trend. It does not produce a constructive growth of personality. In this connection it should be noted that Jesus never glorified suffering in itself. He did not teach that suffering as such is a value. He tried to overcome suffering in its various forms. Had Jesus been a masochistic individual he would not have resisted the temptation to jump from the pinnacle of the Temple, and there would have been no Gethsemane. Had he been a masochistic individual there might have been a cross, but with a background and under circumstances quite different from those that history has recorded. The human mind is quick to feel the difference between the individual who suffers for his own pleasure and the person who makes a sacrifice for some cause in which humanity itself has something at stake.

From masochism we turn to another form of love, namely, sadism. Sadism is the tendency of personality to find satisfactions, either on the overt sexual level or on the emotional level, through making others suffer. The sadistic person is cruel, though he is usually able to find rational reasons for his cruelty.

Sadism may be expressed in the same religious symbols as masochism, but with a different emphasis and content. The idea of a wrathful, punishing God is appealing to the sadistic individual, but in his thinking the wrath of God is always directed toward someone else. The sadistic person tends to minimize the benevolent aspect of God in favor of the cruel aspect. The God of Puritanism is largely a sadistic deity. Persons patterning their lives on such a God find stimulation and encouragement to develop this side of their personalities. Sadism, like masochism, exists in varying degrees of strength in most human beings, and may be either elaborated and destructively directed through religious symbols or controlled and neutralized through their use.

Numerous religious symbols give an opportunity for the expression and elaboration of sadistic trends. The Fundamentalist-Modernist controversy involved the expression of sadism on each side. The controversy between science and religion likewise gave ample opportunity for the expression of sadistic trends. The tendency in some religious persons to glory in the idea that others will be punished for their sins and the elaboration of the symbol "hell" in terms of eternal damnation and punishment for others also may be cited as illustrative of sadistic trends in religion.

That there is a cruel element in all of life, no one with any capacity for realism will deny. One does not break the laws of the inner or of the external world without suffering. And there are cruel aspects of nature that operate irrespective of man. This is part of the problem of suffering with which religion must deal. Religious symbols, therefore, are capable of developing an unbalanced elaboration and structuralization of this tendency in personality.

It is not the true function of religion to repress sadism. This only leads to its expression in disguised and unhealthy forms. Thus a person may not be aware of any desire to inflict suffering on others, but may actually be very cruel under the guise of "following the truth," or of "protecting the standards of society," or of "fighting for the cause of Christ." Repressed sadism, expressing itself under the guise of religious ideals, has frequently played into the hands of masochistic persons. Many martyrs have been masochistic persons, but their persecutors have been sadistic, with their cruelty carefully rationalized by religious symbols.

It is rather the function of religion to lead persons to become aware of the cruel aspect of their personality and to direct that energy toward constructive ends. Fortunately for all of us, the world is far from perfect, and there is much of an evil nature that needs to be destroyed and much constructive work that needs to be done. There is always the danger that religion, as well as other cultural forces, will help people to rationalize their cruelty under the guise of ideals rather than understand it and direct it constructively. When religion influences people to direct their cruelty toward other persons, it is failing in its larger purpose, and the suffering of others is used as a source of pleasure. This results in a failure on the level of social integration; it divides man and man, and it moves in the direction of individual and social pathology. When religion leads men to express their destructive tendencies toward evils that threaten the life or welfare of the group, it is serving a constructive and healthy purpose. But to do this its symbols must be balanced in both usage and content. They must apprehend and express the meaning of life as a whole, not some particular part of the whole.

Cruelty is indeed one aspect of life that finds expression in both man and nature. But it is obviously not the character of the whole of reality. In all of life there is a benevolent, kindly, tender element. This has been grasped and expressed in many religious symbols, such as the Fatherhood of God, the brotherhood of man, love for both God and man, forgiveness, mercy, and others. Through such symbols, properly used, this constructive side of human nature may be stimulated and developed and the cruel side neutralized. Such development is necessary for both individual and social welfare. The masochistic individual uses religious symbols to justify the sacrifice of his own interests for those of others, while the sadistic individual sacrifices others for his own satisfaction. Each is destructive of personality, as each represents only a partial aspect of life and one that is not capable of producing integration.

There is a more mature kind of love, which is centered primarily in persons. In the kinds of love of which we have been speaking it is the act of suffering that is loved; the persons involved are incidental. This more mature kind of love consists in feelings of positive good will toward others, and satisfactions are derived in making it possible for others to find satisfactions. It involves a feeling of tenderness toward others and of fidelity to others. It enables the individual to seek his place among others in mutually helpful relationships, and offsets the impulse to use others as a means toward his own ends. This kind of love may be developed in sufficient strength to neutralize impulses of cruelty and to become the motivation for positive living. Religious practices and symbols may play a large part in this development, and religion fails in its major function if this does not occur.

Christianity has placed emphasis on the teaching of Christ

in regard to love. But to a large extent this has been more verbal than real. The basic problems involved in the development of the capacity to love in the true Christian sense and the mature psychological sense have been ignored or neglected. These problems have been largely left to the psychologists, and psychoanalysis has made a large and valuable contribution at the point of discovering some basic realities in the nature of love. The concept of love in religion has frequently been given a sentimental interpretation, incapable of intelligent application or of serving as a strong motivating force within the personality.

One of the reasons for this ineffectiveness is the attitude which religion has held so long in regard to a large component of the total love impulse, namely, the sexual component. Religion, under the influence of persons who were more pathological than healthy in their love relationships, interpreted sex as evil and sinful. This negative emphasis produced a blindness in regard to the relationship of the sexual component to the love impulse which it sought to develop. The experience of Mary Jones illustrates our point, and it represents a problem that is all too common. The religious interpretation of love that she had been taught and under which her personality had developed was such that it could not integrate the sexual component in her experience.

While maintaining this negative attitude toward the sexual component of the total love impulse, Christianity emphasized the sacredness of the marriage relationship. But again, much of this emphasis was verbal rather than real. The incongruity involved in condemning the biological basis of marriage while emphasizing its sacredness could only produce many unhappy and unhealthy persons and marriages.

Persons familiar with recent development in religion will recognize that we have been describing a situation that is largely in the past and that many churches today are active in the field of sex education and are teaching sound concepts in regard to sex. But the problem of religion and of personality is too deep and complex to be handled by education alone, beneficial as this may be. The problem in each case is that of the relationship of the person as a whole with other persons. In marriage sex is part of this relationship. The love that religion exalts differs from the love of psychologically mature married persons at one major point—it is desexualized. This fact has often led religious persons to speak of "spiritual" love and "physical" love. But such symbols suggest a dichotomy in persons that is not in harmony with psychological fact, and as in the case of Mary Jones, they are often set over against each other in irreconcilable conflict.

Neither the kind of love that leads to a creative and satisfying marriage nor the kind that Christianity teaches is to be derived chiefly through educational processes, whether sex education or religious education. The capacity for such love is an outgrowth of personality development. Such personality development depends primarily on the living relationships between persons. The relationships between the child and the parent are the most significant in this development, but other relationships should not be excluded. Christian literature abounds with statements asserting the close relationship of religion and the family, and the importance of wholesome family life for religion. But such statements may only serve to cloud the real issues and to conceal unhealthy trends under religious symbols and sanctions. Emphasis on the value of the family as an institution to religion as an institution is all too often a means of diverting attention from the actual psychological realities in family relationships. Many persons have become mentally ill as the result of family relationships that have been accepted as Christian. The religious commandment of honor to father and mother may be interpreted in a manner justifying submission to a cruel and dominating parent, or to a very possessive parent who strangles a child's personality through a selfish love. Religion must always and continually clarify the meaning of its symbols in terms of actual relationships between persons and the effect of these relationships on the individuals concerned. And it must develop techniques aimed at creating healthy personal relationships. Any values that the family as an institution holds for religion as an institution rest ultimately on the effectiveness of religion in helping individuals create the kind of family relationships in which persons may grow to the place where they are capable of loving their neighbors as themselves. Unless religion functions creatively in this basic area of human relationships, all efforts on the institutional level to inculcate the ideal of love will continue to be as ineffective as they have been in the past. The preaching of love from the pulpit cannot by itself overcome actual conditions and relationships that breed hostility.

Many practical problems are involved in the kind of love relationships that persons express in their religion. Important among these problems is that bearing on the work of the minister.

The kind of love dominating a person's religious symbolism will find expression in his relationships to the minister. If this love is of a dependent kind, there will be an endeavor to lean heavily on the minister. Whatever way of life the minister teaches, it will have a powerful influence on such persons. Some clergymen welcome this kind of relationship and over a period of time build up a large constituency on this basis. If the love is of a sadistic nature, the individual is likely to be highly critical of the clergyman, constantly seeking to thwart him or hamper his work, but always for idealistic or religious reasons. The cruel element will be well rationalized.

Reactions to sermons, though apparently objective, are usually influenced by the dominant trend in a person's feelings. Thus, a masochistic individual will greatly enjoy a sermon soundly condemning people for their sins. Such persons revel in the feeling of sinfulness, and may consider the effectiveness of a sermon solely on the basis of its power to punish them for their sins. On the other hand, the sadistic individual will be pleased by a sermon soundly condemning others, perhaps some particular group, but at the same time making him feel self-righteous. The sadistic person will be little moved by sermons on forgiveness or love of enemies, unless he is moved against the preacher for dealing with such themes. The person who feels frustrations in the area of love, or is rather dependent and childish in his love relationships, will enjoy sermons that are sentimental and emphasize the child-parent relationship in connection with God.

The same principles hold for the preacher himself. Clergymen with a strong sadistic trend in their personalities will be greatly thrilled with the opportunity to condemn persons for their sins, and may even mistake the emotional glow which they experience for a manifestation of the Holy Spirit. Such clergymen may justify their condemnatory preaching by identifying themselves with a conception of the Old Testament prophets that greatly magnifies the severity of these ancient seers. On the other hand, the preacher with a strong masochistic trend is likely to overemphasize the painful and sacrificial elements of life and to deal constantly with themes involving the idea of man's sinfulness and unworthiness. These and similar ideas will be very realistic to him, and without his being aware of what is happening, he will tend to deal with them constantly. Likewise, the clergyman who has not outgrown infantile feelings of dependence on parental affection and authority may transfer these to God, and will work out these feelings in his sermons. Such sermons will be of a sweetness-and-light variety, will present a naïve view of life and of religion, and will avoid realistic issues. They will satisfy certain members of his congregation, but they will not provide any basis for the emotional and religious growth of personalities striving toward maturity or trying to deal realistically with the problems of everyday life.

Other church problems and activities, and the work of the clergyman and his relationship with his parishioners, might be discussed from the same point of view, but this would carry us away from our present purpose. We have entered into this discussion to illustrate certain principles involved in religious symbolism and its usage. It should be repeated that much more work needs to be done on these problems than has yet been done. There is no cut-and-dried solution for any of these problems. In the next chapter we shall indicate certain fundamental approaches to the whole problem of the relationships between religion and health, of which the situations just discussed are only a part.

The use of religious symbols to work out other emotional tendencies or traits is a fruitful field for exploration. The feeling of inferiority, for example, may be either magnified or alleviated by religion. Or, religion may be used to build up a compensating feeling of superiority. Likewise, the development of submissive tendencies in personality may be either encouraged or discouraged by religion. On the other side, the drive for power may be fulfilled through religion or religion may help a person to cope with this trait in a more constructive manner. Religion may be used to overcome or to confirm a passive attitude toward life, or it may stimulate and justify an overaggressive attitude. Extremes in either direction are unhealthy. On the other hand, antagonism to religion may be an expression of exaggerated hostility and a means of self-justification by attacking symbols standing for the ideal. Antireligion may be just as pathological as overreligiosity. Religion may foster the tendency to withdraw from relationships with others through a fear of being tempted or led astray by them, or by fostering feelings of self-righteous aloofness. This is definitely unhealthy, even though a person engages in solitary religious exercises. The more private and isolating religion becomes, the more pathological it becomes. Religion, to be healthy, must be socializing. Religion may also be an outlet for frustrations arising from many sources. Boisen has found that there is a close relationship between economic depression and the rise of highly emotional religious sects in this country.[1] Then there is the confused individual who goes from one church to another seeking help for inner problems, and finding none, eventually finds his place in the congregation of a mental hospital.

These, and many other such problems, illustrate the fact that religion is a powerful technique for dealing with man's emotional relationships and problems. Organized religion today has lost sight of this fact, and has not developed its methods or message in a manner that makes it as competent as it should be in this area. In the techniques and content of religion, as these influence emotions, there is a powerful influence for either health or illness. The great need today is for a recognition of the problem and a development of religion in a way that will lead men to wholeness and health.

CERTAIN PSYCHOLOGICAL PROCESSES AND THEIR EXPRESSION IN RELIGIOUS SYMBOLS

In the previous chapter mention was made of certain psychological processes which serve the individual whose relationships are based on the ways of escape. These processes are referred to in many psychology texts as mental mechanisms or as mechanisms of adjustment. In others, they are referred to as dynamisms, a word that is more accurate because it conveys the idea that these processes are dynamic in nature. In other words, they represent a portion of mental energy which is being utilized in a given direction or in a specific manner, for the general purpose of reducing inner tensions or of effecting an adjustment to some life problem. As such they are to be found in a mild form in all normal persons and in exaggerated forms in pathological persons. It should be kept in mind that, except in persons capable of some insight into themselves, they function below the level of consciousness. We shall now discuss the most important of these processes, particularly as they find expression in religion.[2]

One of these dynamisms is repression. Repression, mentioned several times in Section One, is a process through which ideas, feelings, or memories that would be painful or terrifying to the individual are excluded from consciousness. Elements of the mind responsible for repression operate below the level of consciousness. The person does not consciously know that he has repressed a painful memory.

Repression absorbs a great deal of energy that should be free for constructive activity. It involves the blocking of dynamic trends within the personality by other dynamic trends. Energy which should be directed toward the outside world is thus consumed in inner conflict of which the person is not aware.

Repression is the product of a negative conscience. However, it should be noted that a negative conscience may also operate on the conscious level. The individual may feel an impulse, but conscience may say, "Thou shalt not." This conscious checking of an impulse is best referred to as suppression.

It should be clear that repression operates against the need of the personality for insight and understanding. It serves the purposes of the will not to know and, in extreme instances, of the will not to live. Repression and insight are two contrary ways of dealing with painful or terrifying reality.

Religious symbols and techniques may be used for either purpose. To the extent that religion fosters a negative conscience it fosters repression. To the extent that it fosters a positive conscience it releases energy for real achievements and leads the person to deal honestly and frankly with reality.

Out of their experience with strong authority some persons have developed a severe, repressive conscience. Such a conscience and its negative values may find structuralization through religious symbols. God, for example, may be thought of as a cosmic counterpart of such a conscience. Religion dominated by a stern, punishing deity can be nothing but repressive.

It is interesting to note that Jesus emphasized the benevolent aspects of deity and the experience of forgiveness as a means of release from repressive, ill-producing guilt. Religion as insight and co-operation cannot be repressive. Its function is that of releasing the personality for creative work and satisfying personal relationships. The joy of living can never be the product of a repressive religion; it is found only to the extent that reality can be accepted and understood, and the positive aspects of personality neutralize the negative.

Repressed feelings or memories do not lie dormant. They create tensions within the organism and find expression in disguised forms. Thus repressed elements of the personality may find expression in physical symptoms, in mental symptoms, or in social behavior of an antisocial variety.

An earlier chapter has illustrated the production of physical illness by repressed feelings. Here we wish to point out that such symptoms may be reinforced by religion. Thus the illness may be interpreted as a punishment from God or as occurring for some special, divine purpose. It may be considered as a "cross" that one has to carry. In this idea there may be sufficient satisfaction to counteract any tendency to recover. Or, such illness may bring out feelings of rebellion in a person and lead him to feel that God and the universe are unjust. Persons who take this interpretation will enjoy their illness quite as much as those who accept it as a "cross." Of course, they will not permit themselves to be conscious of this enjoyment. Chronic illness, emotionally produced, may be supported by such religious interpretations. For this reason clergymen need a thorough clinical training, lest their ministrations defeat their avowed purpose. Clergymen may easily run afoul of the exaggerated need for attention and sympathy that may be present in such persons, and should understand that they do not really help such patients by giving sympathy.

Just as repressed feelings are in some cases converted into physical symptoms, so in others they are converted into highly emotional outbursts of behavior. Hysterical behavior, involving intense emotional excitement, is rather well known. When this is stimulated by religion, the Holy Roller type of religion may result. Such religion may be considered in some cases as an emotional safety valve, though in others it definitely leads to the elaboration of pathological trends. Individuals indulging in it might express the same energy in either more constructive or more destructive ways. Respectable religion, however, has washed its hands of responsibility for such manifestations and tends to be critical of them. However, from the standpoint of health, such religious activity is symptomatic of severe frustrations and repressions. Behind it are serious problems in personal and social living. Organized religion cannot justifiably wash its hands of responsibility in relation to these problems. It should accept such manifestations as symptomatic of sickness in individuals and in the culture, and try to deal with the causes of this illness.

Another dynamism is known as displacement. Displacement is a process in which the emotion associated with a given idea is shifted to another idea or object, one more acceptable to the ego. A person may be unable to accept the fact that he hates his father and may shift this hatred to some other person, say his employer. A person disappointed in love may suddenly shift his affections to another person who in some minor way resembles the orginal lover. Displacement is a process through which conflict is resolved and emotional tension is directed toward a substitute object or idea. This substitute then takes on new significance to the individual.

Displacement occurs frequently in everyday life. When feelings originating in some socially unacceptable idea are displaced to a more socially acceptable idea, the process of social adjustment may be promoted and emotional tension released. In times of war it is undoubtedly true that much hatred becomes displaced to the enemy. If the emotional tension is strong, the substitute idea or object will take on a significance quite in excess of its real value, and the person may find himself involved with some idea or activity far beyond objective justification. When this becomes exaggerated, it leads to personality illness. A practical test of displacement is whether or not it renders an individual's social adjustments more or less difficult.

Displacement is frequent in religion, in both normal and pathological forms. Clergymen, without being aware of the psychological meaning of their endeavors, frequently try to get their parishioners interested in some particular cause. This may be done on an objective and wholesome basis or it may operate through the displacement process. If interest is irrational and excessive, it is almost sure to involve displacement. The rabid prohibitionist may be one who has displaced certain childhood guilt in regard to oral behavior to the problem of alcoholic indulgence by others. Aggressive feelings are easily displaced through religious symbols. Hymns such as "Onward, Christian Soldiers" and "The Son of God Goes Forth to War" are effective at this point.

Religious symbols often are used to displace guilt. In ancient Hebrew religion guilt was displaced to the sacrificial lamb. Some Christian doctrines of the Atonement displace the guilt of humanity to Christ, through whose suffering atonement is considered to be made. Displacement is always involved in the person who feels a strong sense of guilt over some small and insignificant act, or in general, where the feelings of guilt are out of proportion with the significance of the act. This may be developed to pathological proportions.

Fear and hate may be displaced through religious symbols. Fear or hatred of a parent may be displaced to God, and the individual may fear the punishment of God or express strong hatred toward God. A childish feeling of dependence on God, which relieves the individual of personal responsibility, is a displacement of childish love for the parents. The erotic element in personality may be displaced through religion, as is evidenced by certain mystics whose experiences were unquestionably erotic in part, or in such songs as "I Came to the Garden Alone."

It is through the process of displacement that Freud finds a close relationship between ritualistic practices of compulsive neurotics and religious ritual. In the compulsive neu-rotic some ritualistic act, such as washing the hands, becomes extremely important and necessary because feelings of guilt and anxiety are displaced to these practices. The individual is compelled to go through this activity in order to allay anxiety. Guilt and anxiety likewise may be displaced to re-ligious ceremonials; indeed, it is quite understandable that this should happen. But this is a perversion of religious rit-ual. Ritual is then used for the purposes of repression and escape; not for those of insight and co-operation. Religious ritual is elaborated and performed in order to allay guilt and anxiety; not in order to discover a new orientation to life, which would include a more realistic solution of the guilt-producing conflict. Freud has been severely criticized because of his statement that religious ceremonials are a form of mass compulsive neuroses. But they may become just this, and will escape this fate only as the deeper psychological problems involved in religion and religious symbolism are faced realistically and understood and as religious symbolism and ceremonials are subject to rigid discipline in their use.

In a psychological process known as transference we see a form of displacement that is of significance to religion. The shifting or displacement of the feelings of love from one person to another is called transference. The term "trans-ference" is also used by the psychoanalysts to connote certain relationships between the analyst and his patient, but we are not now thinking of it in this connection.

The ability to shift feelings of love from one person to another at various stages of development or in various situa-tions is necessary for mental health and for the growth of personality. A fixation occurs when such transference does not take place. Transference is made difficult by strong fear or hate toward the loved person or by feelings of guilt in relation to love.

A common illustration of transference is seen in adjust-ment to bereavement. The loss of a loved person by death requires the transference of love to other persons or objects.

Freud has pointed out that this is the purpose of mourning.[3] The period of mourning is one in which love is gradually transferred to other persons, and the strong sense of
loss, accompanied by grief and depression, is neutralized by
the development of a positive interest in other persons or
objects. Freud furthermore points out that the pathological
state known as melancholia is in certain respects closely akin
to normal mourning. Melancholia begins with the loss of a
loved object. This loss is not necessarily due to the death of a
loved person; it may be the loss of money, or the infidelity
of a friend, or the loss of a job. In melancholia, the feelings
attached to the lost object are not easily transferred to other
objects. They become directed to the self, which, in part, ex-
plains the melancholiac's extreme concern for himself and
the fact that he gets great satisfaction in his self-condemna-
tion and feelings of worthlessness. It should be added that
other psychological processes are present in melancholia and
that explaining these processes to the patient in no way
helps him.

The process of transference takes place frequently through
religion and religious symbols. Feelings of love are transferred to religious objects, such as the Virgin Mary, Christ,
or God. The effect of this on the personality is determined
by the nature of the transferred feelings and by the manner
in which the symbols are used. A gushy, sentimental type of
religion will result from the transference of frustrated love
to Christ, and the erotic element in such person's religion is
likely to be obvious to the trained observer.

The transference phenomenon is behind some sudden religious conversion experiences. It is seen in certain religious
cures of alcoholism. Some individuals who find expression
of their love impulses in drinking, under the influence of
intense guilt and a sense of hopelessness, are able to "surrender" themselves to God. Such surrender means psychologically the transference of affections to a religious personage, Christ or God, toward whom the individual finds himself
able to express his particular kind of love without guilt

or fear of rejection. A similar phenomenon is seen in a man who had a long record of criminal behavior growing out of intense conflict involving love and hate for his father. Through a religious experience his tendency to criminal behavior was completely reversed. His feelings of frustrated love were transferred to God. In the belief that God had a place for him in the work of the world he found a reversal of the sense of worthlessness acquired from his father. God became the object of his affections; his hostility was redirected in activities that his religion approved. While some aspects of his religion might be open to criticism from various points of view, its personal and social value must be recognized.

The process of transference is likewise found in many religious healings. The cures attained at Lourdes and other such shrines, as well as similar phenomena found in other sections of Christianity, are to be at least partially explained on this basis. Dr. Smiley Blanton has made a medical and psychiatric study of certain cures achieved at Lourdes.[4] In discussing a particular patient, he writes: "Now in this sick man, and in similar sick people who go to Lourdes the important thing, we think, is that they have reached the limit of their emotional and physical capacities to adjust to the demands of their illness. For some reason inherent in their own psychological functioning they cannot any longer accept life and yet they cannot quite accept death. Physically their libidinal drive is what may be termed reversible (because it does reverse itself) but their ego has reached a state of depletion so nearly complete that they themselves have not the capacity to reverse it. In our opinion, it is only when they have reached this state of complete surrender that they can be cured by such a transference—in this case to the Virgin Mother Mary who, they feel, intercedes for them with the Creator Himself. It is now possible for the patient to give up his fear of love; to be willing to accept it without a sense of guilt and without reservation. He surrenders also his

aggression towards his mother and his fear of aggression towards himself."

The transference of affections to religious objects may
result in individual and social values; or it may lead to an
unhealthy use of religion if the displaced feelings are overly
intense or infantile. Understanding of this psychological
process as related to both personality and religious symbols
enables the religious worker to discriminate between constructive and destructive uses of religious symbols and their
effects on personality. Changes in personality occurring
through transference to religious objects are frequently dra-
matic and spectacular. For this reason their true significance
may be missed and the pattern involved may be overeval-
uated and made a norm for others who are psychologically
unable to use it or who do not need to use it. It should
be remembered that this is not a process which can be
achieved by the conscious exercise of will, but may be
achieved through religious symbols operating on a susceptible personality. The Oxford Group Movement relies heavily and unconsciously on this psychological process.

Another psychological process of importance to both health
and religion is that known as reaction formation. Sometimes
it is known as overcompensation. Reaction formation is a
psychological process through which are developed conscious
attitudes and behavior diametrically opposed to repressed
impulses. It involves consciously assuming a virtue in order
to conceal a wish that would lead in the opposite direction.
Thus an individual with strong sexual repressions may assume a conscious attitude of extreme purity or prudishness
and may engage in activities aimed at suppressing the interest or activities of others in sexual matters. A mother who
feels hostile toward her child may develop strong conscious
feelings of anxiety in regard to the child as a reaction against
her repressed hostility. A father severely punishes his son
for masturbation, but completely forgets that he mastur-
bated in his boyhood. His severe punishment is a reaction

against the guilt which he feels in relation to his own past experience and which he has repressed.

Reaction formation is thus a defense against unacceptable feelings or wishes through behavior or attitudes that reverse them. As such it may lead to some social values, and it becomes pathological only in its exaggerated forms. However, it always involves the playing of a conscious role that does not harmonize with deeper realities. In other words, it may ease emotional tension, but it does not provide a basis for integration. In some instances it may be described as assuming a virtue in order to conceal a vice. It is the psychological process involved in much hypocrisy. Sometimes an individual boldly and knowingly "puts on a front" to cover up some weakness. In other instances the individual is not aware of his inner processes; he is aware only of an intense interest in some particular idea or activity.

Reaction formation is a psychological process in which religious symbols become involved, and which may be either elaborated or controlled and reduced through religion. A frequent expression in religion is the "holier-than-thou" attitude. Another is the pharisaical attitude, an emphasis on minor virtues and practices that conceals deficiencies in regard to more significant matters. The religious zealot and reformer is likely to be a person in whom there is a strong reaction against inner guilt and anxiety. The attempt to force others to reform or to restrict the lives of others by rigid rules is frequently a way of avoiding a realistic facing of unacceptable impulses in oneself and an effective way of expressing hostility in the guise of moral idealism. Likewise an overmoralistic attitude toward others is a convenient way of diverting one's attention from inner impulses that are unacceptable. Thus, under the guise of purity and idealism, a woman wanted to have a clergyman relieved of his parish duties because he gave the young people a lecture on sex. All these and other forms of reaction formation may be encouraged through religious symbols and practices. In fact, such attitudes are frequently exalted by religious groups.

Hypocrisy is always a problem in religion. It is something much more easily seen in others than in oneself. To see it in oneself would be painful. Furthermore, it eases inner tensions and produces feelings of comfort which remove the incentive toward understanding. Religion at its best has always looked upon hypocrisy as something morally indefensible. Today it should be looked upon as symptomatic of an unhealthy inner condition.

Reaction formation is also involved in the Pollyanna type of religion. The sweetness-and-light brand is an effective way of avoiding harsh reality and of covering up one's true feelings. Overemphasis on "beauty, goodness, and truth" is a convenient way of blinding oneself to ugliness, evil, and falsehood.

Many are the handicaps which human beings face. Sometimes the only solution of a handicap is to build up some compensating activity or interest. At other times, individuals succeed in directly overcoming handicaps by rigid discipline and great effort. But problems of this kind have to be considered on their own merit and generalizations are dangerous. Because a deaf Beethoven wrote beautiful music is no reason to suppose that all deaf people can do likewise. A great deal of loose advice and false encouragement is given in regard to such problems, and in the end this may be cruel and detrimental. Advising a person to react against a handicap may be as harmful as advising him to withdraw from life because of it.

The crux of the problem lies in whether or not the individual has been helped to accept the reality of the situation. It is the inner attitude toward the handicap that determines the use of compensatory activity. This activity may be used to overcome or compensate for the handicap; or it may be used to repress feelings of bitterness and anxiety in regard to the handicap. If the latter is true, the interest in the activity will be greatly intensified; the activity is likely to be carried on in an irrational manner and the individual will remain sensitive and easily subject to additional psychic injury if criticized or frustrated.

To make this discussion more concrete, we cite the case of a girl who suffered a leg paralysis through an injury early in childhood. Rather than help her accept the handicap, she was told by her mother that she could never be like other girls. She reacted against feelings of bitterness and hate by developing the opposite personality qualities. She was sweet, courageous, and always looked on the bright side. Her school-teacher described her approvingly as a Pollyanna, and the clergyman used her as a shining example of the spiritual conquest of physical handicaps. In adolescence the girl met a new emotional crisis. Under the additional strain the sweetness and courage proved to be merely veneer. Actually she was a very weak person, though through no fault of her own. Her virtues were not genuine achievements; they were reactions against her true inner feelings of hate and anxiety, which found open and undisguised expression on the wards of a mental hospital. The development of the external appearance of virtues as a cover for an inner volcanic condition is never a basis for health.

In order to deal properly with the use of religion in the elaboration and structuralization of the process of reaction formation, those responsible for religious leadership need to be able to recognize and evaluate it in individual persons. Persons whose religion is dominated by this process may get into positions of leadership and thus encourage similar religious practices in others, particularly in adolescents. Here, again, there is no cut-and-dried solution.

It should be noted that Jesus met many instances of this kind of religion. The Pharisees with their emphasis on externals; the individual who tried to take the mote out of his brother's eye when there was a beam in his own eye; the person who wanted his debts forgiven, but who demanded payment from his debtors; the individual who cleansed the outside of the cup but neglected the inside; the wolves in sheep's clothing, and others. The emphasis of Jesus was on the need of being honest and genuine in one's relationships. He did not try to force righteousness on others or to reform others. He helped where others permitted him to help, and he influenced others by the genuine qualities of his own life. He did not emphasize externals; he constantly pointed to inner realities. But teaching as he did through the medium of insight symbols, his words are capable of perversion by persons whose religion is quite the reverse of his.

The next dynamism to be discussed is known as rationalization. Rationalization is grounded in the human need for self-justification and consists in developing good and acceptable reasons to conceal real but unacceptable motives. It is another means of defense and operates against the need for insight. Persons who have good, conscious reasons for their behavior always believe they have true insight. But the good reason may not be the real reason. Rationalization is thus a common form of self-deception. It is a process of substituting fictitious rational motives for real but unconscious, irrational motives. It is a way of defending repressed wishes by justifying their gratification on rational grounds.

Everyday life is full of rationalizations. Advertisers are constantly helping people to rationalize the purchase of something they want but do not really need or cannot afford. Hostility is easily rationalized by appealing to ideas of justice or patriotism. The reformer rationalizes his activities by the theory that he must protect the morals or welfare of others. Individuals who are dependent in a childish way may rationalize their behavior in the idea that the world owes them a living. The criminal may rationalize his antisocial behavior on the grounds that society has not given him a square deal. The conservative and radical alike build rational structures to justify their behavior, especially when it is criticized.

Rationalization may occur in mild or extreme form. It may be an occasional or an habitual way of meeting problems. When it becomes habitual and extreme it becomes dangerous. It is always a way of avoiding insight and of escaping from some reality. It is the basis of delusions found in the mentally ill.

Religious symbols serve effectively the process of rationalization. Religious reasons may be used to justify behavior and to conceal the true motives. The woman whose desire to die was stronger than the medicine of the physician rationalized her behavior by thinking that it was the will of God that she should die. The person who accepts a religious view on the authority of another person will find it necessary to develop arguments to support his belief. The person who is rebellious toward religion will feel it necessary to find good reasons for rejecting it.

In previous chapters we have spoken of the overintellectualization of religion. This takes place through the process of rationalization. Thus religion found itself in conflict with science, and immediately set about rationalizing its beliefs. There was much rationalization on the Fundamentalist and Modernist sides of this controversy, as well as on the scientific side.

Theology is constantly in danger of becoming nothing more than a series of rationalizations. Theology represents the rational side of religion. But religion, as we have said, involves the total personality as well as its cosmic environment. The theologian needs to be constantly on the alert lest his effort to think about the fundamental problems of life become nothing more than the rationalization of his feelings. There is a great difference between a living theology, which reveals man's inner being, and a dead theology, which conceals living processes behind a screen of rationalizations. When religious beliefs and symbols are used to allay anxiety rather than to discover the realities that create the anxiety, there will be a constant tendency toward overelaboration and overintellectualization. Up to a certain point of development that is difficult to define, theological structure serves the purposes of growth and integration. Elaboration beyond that point serves only to conceal unacceptable feelings, particularly guilt and anxiety. On the whole, a simple theological structure is more healthy than a highly elaborated one, though of course personality needs in this respect differ. But a simple theological structure may be just as rigid and arbitrary as one that is highly elaborated, and may be used to express and defend a view of life that is naïve and unhealthy. The task of theology is to help man adjust to reality through the use of reason, not to use reason for the purpose of rationalizing unhealthy tendencies within himself.

Rationalization serves the purpose of the will not to know. It shifts the attention from inner realities to symbols. It avoids the irrational element in personality by overvaluing the logical arrangement of symbols. But the deeper elements in personality are irrational. Conflicts and frustrations that lead to illness are concerned with these irrational elements. In the mentally ill person who has systematized delusions of persecution is found the use of rationalized beliefs to conceal destructive, irrational elements in the personality. A theological system may function in a somewhat similar manner. Theological systems and delusional persecutory systems sometimes have one thing in common. If the main assumptions are granted, the systems will be found to be logically watertight. Theology, on the other hand, may be used as a means of facing and understanding the irrational elements in experience and of finding a mature, wholesome solution to the problems which they present.

The individual who seeks to develop a way of life on the basis of understanding and co-operation will find ample outlet for his rational powers in striving toward these ends. The individual whose way of life is based on escape or rebellion will find that reason also can be used for these ends. Mere logic is no criterion of healthy or wholesome relationships with reality.

Still another dynamism is known as projection. Projection is a psychological process through which the individual's perceptions of objects or persons are determined by unacceptable feelings within himself. External reality becomes something of a screen on which are projected feelings and desires that the individual cannot accept as part of himself.

Like other dynamisms, projection occurs frequently in everyday life. The individual who is quick to recognize in others faults which he cannot see in himself is projecting. Much criticism and prejudice is the result of projection. A person with dishonest tendencies may become suspicious of others. Likewise a person with unacceptable sexual impulses may read his own motives into the behavior of others. An individual who is failing in his work may project his feelings on the employer and blame the employer. There are many individuals in all walks of life who are sure that they do not get ahead because others are holding them back.

Projection is seen also in many forms of mental illness, and is the primary dynamism in paranoid disorders. These patients develop ideas of persecution. They feel that they are being persecuted by certain enemies. These delusions are formed by the projection of intense hostility on other people, who then are seen in the role of dangerous enemies. The projection process is rationalized by the delusional ideas.

Religious symbols are convenient instruments for the projecting process. Projection may so dominate the use of religious symbols that the individual's view of the world is quite out of harmony with reality. The same situation may occur, of course, without the use of religious symbols. But the point here is that religious symbols of themselves are no guarantee of a view of the world that harmonizes with reality. In a previous chapter the use of religious symbolism to convey the nature of both internal and external reality was discussed. Projection interferes with this fundamental characteristic of religious symbolism, and uses symbols for the expression of inner reality in external guise. Inner reality is not honestly recognized for what it is—it is seen as a quality of the external world. Thus the perception of the nature of both internal and external reality is distorted. This distortion always has a destructive aspect, as it is the unacceptable tendencies which the individual has need to project.

The individual who has faced and become reconciled to his own inner nature, and who has gained a large measure of objectivity in regard to his own inner world, will be in a position more accurately to perceive the nature of the external world. The search for truth must begin with oneself.

Belief in a personal devil at one time served as a useful, but not always wholesome, symbol for projection of unacceptable impulses. Satan was responsible for sin. This symbol could be of real value for individuals to whom it had meaning, provided it was handled properly. One of the earliest illustrations of projection in religious records is the story of Adam and Eve. Adam projected his guilt on Eve, and Eve in turn projected her guilt on the serpent. It is interesting to note that even today the serpent is a common symbol of temptation.

Sometimes guilt and the fear of punishment are projected on God. God then becomes the accusing deity who knows one's sin and is preparing punishment. This is a form of externalizing conscience. Sometimes hostility is projected on the church or religion in general. This may express itself in a critical attitude toward the church or in the view that religion is responsible for the ills of humanity. On the pathological level the patient cited by Dr. Boisen, who believed that it was his mission to reconcile God and Satan, was projecting his inner conflict and seeking to solve it in cosmic rather than personal terms.[5]

Projection may play a large part in the relationships between the clergyman and his parishioners. Either may project his guilt or hostility on the other. The clergyman may thus blame the parishioners for the lack of success of the church program. The parishioner may feel that the clergyman is singling him out for condemnation from the pulpit or that the clergyman is interfering unduly with his personal affairs. One instance has come to my attention where a clergyman tore up a sermon after it had been carefully written because he had the insight to discover that it was inspired by the projection of hostility on certain members of his church board. This is a practical example of the value of mental hygiene training for clergymen, combined with the ability to apply it personally.

Behind the projection process there is always the unwillingness or the inability to face some painful, inner reality. The individual gains considerable relief of tension and a strong sense of self-righteousness in falsifying reality in his own favor. This is contrary to the true function and attitude of religion. It operates against the insight usage of religious symbols and is a means of escape rather than co-operation. Once firmly established and structuralized, it is a process that is difficult, if not impossible, to reverse. It is for this reason that paranoid patients are not likely to get well. However, religious symbols, properly used, should lead to a strengthening of the ego and to the reversal of this pattern, provided it is not too strong or has not crystallized to an irreversible degree.

Still another psychological process of significance for both religion and health is that known as identification. Through this process the ego is unconsciously patterned after another who has been taken as an ideal. Identification is to be distinguished from imitation in that the latter is conscious and pertains chiefly to copying the behavior of another. Identification occurs without conscious awareness, and makes fundamental changes in the feelings, ideas, and attitudes of the person concerned.

Identification is a fundamental process in personality development. The first identifications are usually with the parent. The little boy wants to be like his father and in some ways to take the place of his father. The student identifies himself with an admired and respected teacher, and becomes a devotee of the teacher's particular views or unknowingly patterns himself after the teacher's attitudes and behavior. An individual identifies himself with a group, and takes as his own the standards and beliefs of the group. Failure to have a relationship with the father that will make possible an identification on the part of the son will lead to a serious warping of the growing personality.

Identification grows in part out of the child's helplessness and need for a pattern of living. It is the psychological basis for the perpetuation of personality traits in families. "Like father, like son" may be due in part to biological inheritance, but it is also due in part to social inheritance operating through identification. It is also the psychological basis on which can be explained many phenomena which in the past have been credited to a herd instinct. Behind the desire to be like others the process of identification is operative.

Identification is an important process in religion and operates easily through religious symbols. Religion, being so much a matter of relationships between persons and between persons and the universe, utilizes constantly the ability of the individual to identify himself with others, or with an ideal such as Christ. Such identifications are essential to religion as a personal or group experience. The ability to take a co-operative attitude toward life depends in part on the ability to grasp and identify oneself with those realities with which co-operation is essential. At this point there are many problems in the psychology of religion that deserve careful study.

In an earlier chapter it was pointed out that scientific knowledge could be passed on by educational processes, whereas in religion the symbolic tradition could be thus transmitted but not the inner meaning. This has to be achieved by each person for himself. To a large extent it is achieved on the basis of identifications. It is for this reason that the personality of the teacher of religion is of such great significance. The identification of the child with the teacher is far more potent in the development of the child's personality than all the traditional formula that can be uttered. It is for this reason that the personality and mental health of religious workers is much more important than is generally realized. The religious worker whose personality is not attractive and stimulating, and who therefore does not provide a basis for identification, will have little positive effect on his group, except to leave the impression that religion itself is dead and outworn. The religious worker who has definitely unhealthy attitudes and ideas, but a certain attraction in his personality, may stimulate identifications that will lead to the transplanting of unhealthy attitudes and ideas in others. In the psychological process of identification religion and health alike have one of their greatest assets as well as potential liabilities.

Many other illustrations of the process of identification in religion could be cited. Christianity aims directly at the identification of the individual with Christ as the ideal. Prayer and worship may serve a dynamic function in this process. The crux of the problem here is the specific content given to the ideal, and the manner in which the identification is lived out. In the Holy Communion there is a strong symbolic expression of the desire for identification with Christ. Identification with Christ carries with it the identification with the group, with Christ as its leader. Through identification religion seeks to lead persons to the acceptance of super-individual goals and loyalties, to share the common problems and values of the group, and to center their life in purposes and meanings that are cosmic in scope. Here is one of the most powerful, cohesive, and stabilizing forces in the human life, and one which certain political groups have capitalized in a manner far beyond that of the church. Psychological and social processes of a divisive, disruptive nature tend to weaken identification with the group, and serve also to split groups into factions. A weakness of Protestantism has been in the tendency of disruptive elements to identify themselves with Christ, thus sanctioning hostility and aggression under a symbol which originally was one embodying love. In such a cultural situation there can be little positive health. The true function of religion is to neutralize hostility by the development of the affections, not that of drawing off hostility by identification with a love symbol. Here is a point where symbol and reality should not be confused.

Identification, like other processes, becomes pathological when it is overdone. It is one thing to desire to be like Christ; it is quite another to say, "I am Christ." Such complete identification grows out of intense inner conflicts and is definitely a symptom of mental illness. Persons with such ideas should be in mental hospitals. Unfortunately they are not all in mental hospitals. There are other persons whose identification with Christ, while not so extreme, is highly exaggerated and serves to create an ego inflation that is itself a symptom of severe underlying conflict and tension. Such persons may achieve positions of leadership, and they may injure the cause of true religion by their sentimental and sometimes obnoxious assertions that they are "Christians." For the clergyman there is always the danger of an overidentification of himself with Christ, and this leads to the feeling that his words embody a special truth or revelation or should carry an extra weight of influence.

Closely related to the process of identification is that known as idealization. Idealization is a process resulting in what is commonly known as hero worship. It is to be seen in the person who has fallen in love and is unable to see any faults in his beloved. It involves an overevaluation of some object or person because of the transference of love from the self to the object. While through identification the self is altered to conform to a pattern set by another, in idealization the self finds something on which its affections can be centered. Just as the person finds it difficult to criticize himself to the extent that he is in love with himself, so he finds it difficult to criticize the idealized person. Through idealization the idea of perfection is developed.

Idealization is utilized in the development of conscience. In this sense, conscience may be said to be love for a moral ideal or an ideal of moral perfection. The process of idealization should be distinguished from the object of idealization. It is the object rather than the process, and the intensity of the attachment, that determines whether it will result constructively or destructively in the personality.

Idealization is common in religion, and is capable of both healthy and unhealthy application through religion.

Christ is not only a symbol for identification, but also one for idealization. Christianity teaches persons not only to be like Christ, but to love Christ. Indeed, it has made love of Christ basic, in the belief that love is the only basis for identification. But it can be readily seen that it is easy to overdo the process of idealization and create a meaning for religious symbols that carries one dangerously away from reality. Some concepts of the divinity of Christ tend to do this. The doctrine of the virgin birth could have credence in a modern mind only through an exaggeration of the idealizing process. The idealizing process may furnish powerful motivation toward an ideal, but the critical faculties of the personality must be permitted to function in their proper manner if balance is to be maintained. This means first an inner adjustment that reduces the need for an exaggerated form of idealization that throttles the reason.

Worship may be used as a means of discovering the reality embodied in religious symbols. Or it may be used to intensify the tendency to idealize by overemphasis on the symbols to the neglect of reality. The doctrine of the infallibility of the Bible illustrates the overidealization of a religious symbol, and the repression of the critical faculties in relation to that symbol. It involves a literal worship of the Bible. Likewise, overidealization leads to the refusal to alter or modify the meaning or use of any religious symbol. Under the guise of truth or perfection, religious beliefs or moral codes may be crystallized by a superficial kind of reverence that does not get deeper than the symbol itself. As has been pointed out previously, only that person or group that can combine a reverence for its symbols with a capacity for change and revision can remain healthy.

Overidealization is frequently expressed in religion in an intense interest in static moral or theological perfection. Sometimes it finds expression through the symbol "spiritual," which is usually used in contrast with another symbol such as "carnal." It finds expression also in the "goody-goody" kind of person. We recall a young woman who was brought to the hospital in a disturbed condition. She had been conscious all her life that her mother hated her. But her mother had always hid this hatred by conscious reaction against it and by a highly idealized religion that constantly led her to talk about "spiritual things." Discussing her mother's hatred and rejection, the patient ended an uninhibited tirade against the mother with the words, "And she was so spiritual, damn her." All of which indicates that the hypocrisy of such reaction and overidealization may be apparent to those victimized by it.

Idealization and identification are common phenomena in the religion of the adolescent. This is quite readily understood in the light of the two fundamental tasks of adolescence. First, the adolescent is seeking to emancipate himself from parental authority and develop a personality capable of independent relationships with others. Unless he succeeds in this he is likely to follow a way of life based on escape or on rebellion. Secondly, he is faced with the problem of integrating new feelings of love into his personality and of dealing with psychological and physiological tensions that are distinctly new. That the adolescent should identify himself with others, particularly those occupying prestige positions in culture, is only to be expected. Religion offers abundant opportunity for both experiences. Properly guided, religion at this time should become a sort of bridge from childhood to maturity. Improperly directed, it may become an obstacle to the necessary adjustment to reality. The tendency to overidealize is amply illustrated in the experience of Mary Jones. Overidealization provides the groundwork for a later disillusionment, which may result in some unhealthy compromise solution. Institutional forces in religion frequently exploit the strong tendency toward identification and idealization in adolescence for institutional ends, and this can only result, where effective, in either an ambivalent attitude toward the church or a rebellion against it.

Idealization also becomes a problem in clergy-parishioner relationships. There is a strong tendency in many religious persons to consider the clergyman on a moral plane above that of the average person. This means that he is expected to exemplify an almost perfect life or to fulfill expectations beyond his capacity. In other words, it leads frequently to a demand, not so much consciously expressed as constantly implied, that the minister be something that he cannot be. The clergyman is thus under a social pressure to play a role and to present external appearances that may be completely out of harmony with his personality. This is a mental health hazard for the clergyman. It may lead him to bask unconsciously in the false light of hero worship and thus blind him to glaring realities. Or, it may lead him to develop an unnatural and formal kind of goodness, which is neither attractive nor vigorous. Or, he may become irritated, and rebel against his idealizing parishioners, and find himself in constant difficulty with them. People cannot see their idols jump down from the pedestal without being moved to inflict punishment. When overdone and made into a cultural pattern, overidealization becomes unhealthy for both the clergy and the parish. It is an excellent way of encasing a personality in empty symbols, thus thwarting his efforts to deal with harsh or painful reality. One sees some of the practical implications of this in a remark of a patient, who, as she related her story, said, "But these are hardly things for a minister's ears."

The final psychological process to be discussed is known as sublimation. Sublimation may be defined as the diversion of an impulse from its original, socially unacceptable goal to a goal that is more socially acceptable. This diversion may take place through work, play, or some form of artistic creation. Psychoanalysis speaks of sublimation almost entirely in relation to sexual impulses. Jung, who holds a much broader concept of the nature of psychic energy than does Freud, considers this process more in terms of the transformation of energy in excess of purely biological needs to cultural ends. In so far as religion is concerned, we need not pause to debate the issues involved in the differences between the Freudian and Jungian concepts of psychic energy. The function of religion is the diversion or transformation of energy toward goals and values that lead to integration and growth, individually and socially. This can be accomplished without an exact, scientific description of the nature of psychic energy.

The ambivalent attitude of many religious persons toward the Freudian formulations is shown clearly in regard to the concept of sublimation. On the one hand, the Freudian view of the sexual nature of the central drive in personality has been strongly rejected. On the other hand, the doctrine of sublimation has been enthusiastically accepted and in some quarters overdone or misapplied. More than one case is known where individuals were advised to sublimate, when in reality they could have been helped to achieve a much needed and more satisfying direct satisfaction in full harmony with the moral code. But the point is that, unless the Freudian concept of psychic energy, or something similar to it, is accepted, there is no need for a doctrine of sublimation. The two go together. It is interesting to note that religion has become so idealized in some quarters that it has rejected psychological doctrines which are strangely similar in their psychological significance to the religious doctrine of original sin. When realistic, religion has apprehended, through various symbols, the presence in man of impulses requiring deflection from their unrighteous aim to more righteous goals.

Before discussing the relation of religious symbols to sublimation, we shall dispose of a practical problem. The enthusiasm with which the doctrine of sublimation has been accepted in religious quarters has led frequently to its exploitation as an easy, formal solution of sex problems, without ample recognition or understanding of practical difficulties involved. One of these difficulties is the fact that the capacity for sublimation differs in individuals and that probably no one can successfully sublimate completely. Another is the fact that impulses severely repressed cannot be easily sublimated. They are more likely to be expressed in psychological processes that lead to illness. The easy advice to sublimate may be an escape from a problem on the part of the adviser rather than a courageous facing and solving of it. Directly bearing on this problem is a point on which Freud and Jung are in agreement, and one which is pertinent to the use of religious symbols as transformers of energy. It is that sublimation is not a conscious, rational process. As Dr. Ernest Jones points out, a person may engage in given activities spontaneously or upon advice, and in this way initiate the sublimating process.[6] But the process of sublimation is fundamentally an unconscious one; that is, it occurs without the conscious knowledge or control of the person concerned. Jung states the matter thus: "It does not lie in our power to transfer 'disposable' energy at pleasure to a rationally chosen object. . . . It [energy] revolts from any continuous pursuit of the rationally presented possibilities. Psychical energy is indeed a fastidious thing that demands the fulfillment of its own conditions."[7] Sublimation, then, is not the result of rational choice; it occurs as energy becomes diverted spontaneously from an unacceptable to a more acceptable aim. The individual does not consciously "use" sublimation to solve a conflict; the conflict is solved as the individual finds a satisfying activity.

This characteristic of sublimation is fundamental to a consideration of the relation of religion and religious symbols to sublimation. Religious symbols, as already stated, are primarily instruments for the expression of the meaning and value of experience as a whole. Meaning and value involves aims and goals. Religious symbols, especially verbal symbols, are drawn from every phase of life and are capable of expressing, in sublimated form, impulses or energy arising on any level of personal experience. As we have said previously, they operate on the basis of analogy rather than on the basis of logic. It is on this basis that they function as transformers of energy. The symbol, being an analogue of the original aim of the impulse, becomes a channel through which energy is diverted from the original aim to the aim formulated by the symbol. This relationship between impulse and symbol is intuitively felt, not logically created. The symbol becomes alive and meaningful because it is the form through which energy is expressed and value is achieved. Only living religious symbols are capable of serving this function. Dead symbols, as we have defined them, have lost this capacity.

Religion, being concerned with the meaning of life as a whole, is peculiarly fitted to act as a transformer of energy from lower, or primitive, goals to goals involving a fuller development of individuality in harmony with group welfare. For energy or impulses are only part of experience, and they are capable of their highest function only as they are expressed toward goals that are meaningful for the person as a whole. This involves a consideration of environmental relationships, as well as the need for satisfaction. The individual who is at the mercy of his impulses is sick. Such expression of impulses leads to neither personal nor social values, and to no permanent relationships. Psychoanalysts point out that "sublimated love creates more permanent ties than sensual love," and that in order to be lasting "sensual love must either be combined with sublimated tender components or transformed into these."[8] The individual whose impulses are directed or redirected toward goals that serve the welfare of the person as a whole is a healthy, integrated person, capable of developing satisfying and lasting relationships. Religious symbols are capable of expressing meaning on a level that relates the individual to his world. As has been said, they are the means of expressing man's apprehension of ultimate truth and his relationship to it, of man's relationship to man, and of moral law. This means that they are channels through which psychic energy may be expressed toward goals that have high moral, social, and cosmic significance. Alexander, in discussing sublimation, points out that social achievement can allay the sense of guilt, and that it is this social factor, namely, "communication, going beyond the limits of one's own personality," that operates in the sublimating process to relieve the sense of guilt.[9] After a long study of mental illness from the point of view of religion, Boisen concluded that the central evil in the experience of the mentally ill is the sense of isolation arising out of the feeling of guilt.[10] Religion, being concerned with the destiny of the individual, the social group, and the universe, and using symbols capable of fusing these aspects into a whole, is thus capable of raising the expression of impulsive energy toward goals that create high positive meaning and integration, thus removing both guilt and isolation. Religion, especially Christianity, requires that one go beyond the limits of his own personality; that his activity and strivings have significance for more than himself. Religion furthermore provides symbols and techniques which, when properly used, lead to this goal. Religion does not, however, seek to manipulate psychological processes, as one might seek to adjust the mechanism of a clock or as if the person were entirely separate from his surroundings. It seeks to relate man to his universe on the basis of understanding and cooperation and to present objects and values worthy of his affections, worship, and striving. In this way it aims at creating inner equilibrium, or peace.

At this point a certain fallacy in the interpretation of religious symbols can be exposed. It is the tendency to interpret all religion according to a formula found to be true in certain individual experiences. A certain psychoanalytic interpretation illustrates this. The symbol "Father" as used in relation to God leads some analysts to say that God merely replaces the human father and that love for God is merely a childish affection for the parent. That this is true in some cases we would not dispute. It would be expected in those individuals who use religious symbols as a means of concealment and escape. But, as we have tried to show, religious symbols may be used as a means of insight and growth. This means that the symbol "Father" as related to God becomes a means through which an understanding of the individual's relationship to reality is brought to light, and through which new relationships may be formed. The symbol "Father" is indeed an analogue for the expression of impulses originally directed toward the human parent. But, properly used, it is a symbol that resolves conflicts and frees the person for growth toward relationships and values far beyond the level of childish experience. Vital religion leads the individual upward toward goals that are in harmony with the best conceptions of psychological maturity, even though it may originate on a childish level.

Another difficulty which needs to be faced here is the fact that in some persons religion apparently leads to a life of inactivity and withdrawal from society. The use of religion to serve the purpose of escape has already been mentioned. Religious symbols may serve as an outlet for fantasy life as well as for mastering reality. Cases frequently come to light of persons who withdraw from the religious group and from society in general and engage in solitary religious exercises. These exercises—prayer, meditation, and Scripture reading— become an outlet for fantasy in such persons, and strengthen the tendency to withdraw from the real but difficult world into an unreal but pleasurable world that gradually takes on the feeling of reality. This use of religious symbols for escape through fantasy formation may be found in milder forms in persons who receive a strong emotional glow through contemplation of religious symbols, but in whom there is no effort to live out their religion in any way meaningful to the life of the group. In such persons, energy is drained off and satisfactions are achieved through fantasy, not through activities creating real values.

Religion, when it is true to its own function, leads the individual to a way of life based on the principles of insight and co-operation, not on those of evasion and escape. Religious symbols therefore become a means through which energy is directed toward activities in the real world rather than ends in themselves, as fantasy formation makes them. When religion is successful in the transformation of energy it frees the person for constructive work or creative living.

In presenting to mankind the ideas of the Fatherhood of God, the brotherhood of man, and the kingdom of God as an order of society toward which men should strive, Christianity has given a basis for the integration of man's inner and external worlds capable of mobilizing his energy and talents in a way of life that leads to lasting values. Again we repeat, the objects that a man considers to be worthy of his worship define his way of life, and the way of life followed by a person or group inevitably leads to illness or to health. A man's god is more significant for his health than is generally acknowledged.

REFERENCES

1. BOISEN, A. T., "Economic distress and religious experience," *Psychiatry*, 2: 1939, p. 185.
2. The discovery of these processes has been one of the contributions of psychoanalysis, though other schools of psychology are now taking over these concepts for their own use. Readers interested in a fuller elaboration than is given here will find the following works helpful:
   HEALY, WM., BRONNER, AUGUSTA F., and BOWERS, ANNA M., *The Structure and Meaning of Psychoanalysis*. New York, 1930.
   HENDRICKS, IVES, *The Facts and Theories of Psychoanalysis*. New York, 1934.
   HORNEY, K., *The Neurotic Personality of Our Time*. New York, 1937.
   BROWN, J. F., *The Psychodynamics of Abnormal Behavior*. New York, 1940.
3. FREUD, S., "Mourning and Melancholia," *Collected Papers*, Vol. IV, p. 152. London, 1925.
4. BLANTON, SMILEY, "Analytical study of a case at Lourdes," *Psychoanalytic Quarterly*, 9: 1940, pp. 348-362.
5. BOISEN, A. T., *The Exploration of the Inner World*, Chap. 6. Chicago, 1936.
6. JONES, ERNEST, *Papers on Psychoanalysis*, pp. 605 and 606. London, 1923.

7. JUNG, C. G., *Two Essays on Analytical Psychology*, p. 52. London, 1928.
8. HEALY, WM., BRONNER, AUGUSTA F., and BOWERS, ANNA M., *The Structure and Meaning of Psychoanalysis*, p. 250. New York, 1930.
9. ALEXANDER, FRANZ, *The Psychoanalysis of the Total Personality*, pp. 126 and 127. New York, 1930.
10. BOISEN, A. T., *The Exploration of the Inner World*, p. 144. Chicago, 1936.

CHAPTER XI

SOME PRACTICAL CONSIDERATIONS

THE task of this chapter is to summarize the point of view developed in the preceding pages and to indicate some of its practical applications.

Our fundamental thesis is that illness and health are the products of the functioning of the individual as a whole within his total environment. Illness, whether the symptoms are primarily developed on the chemical, physical, psychological, social, or religious level, or a combination of these, is indicative of failure in the process of adjustment of the total person in his environmental relationships. Illness is thus the product of the way of life followed by the individual and the group. The same is true in regard to health, except that health is a positive achievement that is both the result of and the basis for the fulfillment of personality. In either illness or health, religion functions on the level of meaning, value, and purpose, negatively or positively. Meaning, value, and purpose are not philosophical abstractions, but living realities that crystallize experience in terms of the person as a whole. In turn, they modify and influence subsequent experience and the further interpretation of experience. The symbolic structure of religion offers a form through which meaning, value, and purpose are formulated and organized, either negatively or positively, judged from the point of view of personality integration and growth. When true to its character and function, religion seeks the development of inner attitudes toward and interpretations of life experience which in turn become the basis of a way of life leading to the solution of conflict on the basis of co-operation with the fundamental realities of the universe. When not true to its basic character and function, it leads to the development of attitudes and interpretations in which evasion and concealment and escape or rebellion are the dominant trends.

The culture in which a person lives plays a major role in his illness or health. After full recognition is given to the capacity for spontaneity, initiative, and autonomy within the individual, the part played by cultural forces and pressures in molding each personality must be recognized as being significant for health. The culture determines many satisfactions or frustrations; it sets standards, punishes deviations, and rewards adherence to those standards; it seeks to preserve its values and patterns against pressures from individuals who would change them. All these functions, and the manner in which they are carried out, affect the persons in the culture for good or for ill.

On the other hand, personality does affect culture. Some persons accept the culture as it is, or some particular aspect in which they have a special interest, and seek to preserve the status quo. Others seek to break down cultural patterns and values for their own personal gain. Still others, conscious of the great discrepancy between the values that culture holds as desirable and those necessary for the fuller development of personality, seek to change and develop culture constructively.

The impact of the individual on culture is clearly indicated in the persons the group selects as leaders. Beyond the capacity for leadership there is the larger question of the mental health of the leader. The history of humanity is marked by the rise to power of men with the capacity for leadership but with definitely unhealthy attitudes and beliefs, which, because of the power of their leadership and the intense frustrations operating in the culture, they were able to develop into cultural values and patterns which in turn affected the health of their contemporaries and of succeeding generations. The preservation of the freedoms valued by democracy requires that more attention be given to the mental health of leaders in such fields as government, labor, economics, education, and religion. A long step in the right direction is the education of the average citizen so that he will be able to detect at least grossly unhealthy personalities in high places as well as in low, and where he will require sanity and soundness, as well as capacity, in his leaders. On the other hand, it must be recognized that the condition of the emotional life of the members of a culture, rather than their intelligence, will dominate the choice of leaders.

The interrelations between personality and the culture plays a determining role in both illness and health. The health of the individual is inseparably linked with the health of the culture, and vice versa. Behind the conflicts on the level of cultural patterns—in labor, economics, politics, education, and religion—there are conflicts within personalities, and the endeavor of some personalities to break through frustrating patterns in the hope of finding a richer experience. To be sure, many of these conflicts are handled in an irrational and destructive manner. The extent to which this occurs is symptomatic of the degree of illness existing in the culture. The stronger the inner tension the more irrational its expression may become. But the day is rapidly passing when the conflicts within any area of culture may be considered by themselves; they must be viewed in the light of the culture as a whole. Conflicts in one aspect of the culture may produce repercussions in another aspect; for example, economic frustrations may give rise to a highly emotional kind of religious expression. A healthy personality requires a healthy culture, and the illness of individuals today is created more by a sick culture than by disease germs. The integration and growth of personality is determined to a large extent by the kind of values the culture places at the disposal of the individual and the way in which culture permits him to work out his frustrations. On the other hand, the sick individuals create a sick culture. The vicious circle may be broken on either the individual or the cultural level, and both approaches must be used by the forces working for health.

Religion is both an individual experience and a cultural

phenomenon, and as such presents a two-way approach to the basic problems of adjustment which every person faces. Since religion is fundamentally a means through which individuals and groups seek a way of life leading to a solution of life problems and since health and illness are definitely the result of the kind of solution reached, religion, illness, and health are inextricably related at the very center as well as on the periphery of life. The symbols and techniques of religion may be used to foster and reinforce unhealthy tendencies either in individuals or in culture, or they may be used to change either individuals or culture in the direction of health.

The human organism and the cultural setting in which most of us live being what they are, illness is to a certain extent inevitable. The human situation precludes a perfect adjustment. Furthermore, a human being is never adjusted in any final way. Adjustment is a continuing process, and the only thing that can be achieved to any degree of finality is a basis on which progressive adjustments may be made. But adjustment, being a psychological concept, should in religious terminology give way to some such word as "reconciliation," implying as it does a movement in the direction of positive meaning and value, the synthesis of opposing forces or elements in the personality and culture in a manner that leads to the true achievement of value. Psychologically, this is essentially the process of salvation, but contrary to some Christian viewpoints, salvation is never finally or completely achieved, at least not in this life. Likewise, perfect health is an ideal beyond complete achievement. While condemning individuals for being ill is both inhuman and destructive, a sense of individual responsibility for getting well or a desire to get well is essential to recovery. Likewise, on the religious side, a sense of responsibility for the full utilization of one's energies and potentialities and a desire to achieve value in a measure approximating the capacity for achievement are essential to the appropriation of objective realities necessary for salvation. This sense of responsibility and urge toward values must be complemented by understanding the nature and purpose of those realities within and beyond the individual on which he is depending, as well as by the will and ability to relate himself co-operatively to those realities. In all of this only tragedy ensues from the confusion of the symbol for the reality of experience.

The point of view we have been developing contains many practical implications which are highly significant for both medicine and religion and also for allied endeavors such as psychology and social work.[1] Numerous physicians are at work developing various aspects of the practice of medicine on the psychosomatic level.[2] This is a field properly left to the physicians, and we shall not deal with it here. Only one observation will be made. The increasing knowledge and interest of allied professional groups, such as psychologists, clergymen, and social workers, as well as intelligent laymen, should serve as both an encouragement and an aid to physicians interested in this new development in medicine.

In this chapter we shall deal with the implications of the point of view developed in this book, first for the clergyman as a professional worker and second for the relationship of physicians and clergymen. In addition we shall deal briefly with the relation of the clergyman and social worker. We shall not attempt to discuss any of these problems exhaustively. The time is not yet ripe for such treatment. Many of these problems remain to be worked out in actual practice and possible solutions need to be tested in concrete experience. We shall therefore consider our task to be that of indicating avenues through which progress may be made.

SOME PRACTICAL CONSIDERATIONS FOR THE WORK OF THE CLERGYMAN

The first consideration for the work of the clergyman is the fact that through religious ministrations he may actually aid in the development of an illness or make a cure more difficult or impossible. In this he is not alone. He shares this danger with all who work professionally with sick persons and also with friends and relatives. The fact that the physician may become a pathogenic agent has been pointed out by more than one physician.[3] Leaders in the field of social work and nursing also are aware of the problem. The relatively few clergymen who have had the advantage of clinical training during the past decade also understand the danger. Other clergymen have sensed it on the basis of their experience with the ill. But this fact is not so generally recognized by clergymen as it should be, owing largely to the inadequate training that clergymen receive in this highly significant area of their work.

Persons in whose illness an emotional component is either a causative or a complicating factor are usually suggestible. They may be constantly looking for confirmation of the seriousness of their illness, and frequently are experts in misinterpreting a chance remark to mean much more than the speaker implied. For one reason or another they want to be ill and will utilize any opportunity to retard or block recovery. This is equally true of patients suffering from mental or physical symptoms. At the same time they gain certain secondary ends by being ill, and the worker, be he physician or clergyman, must have sufficient understanding and effective techniques to prevent himself from becoming a mere tool for the accomplishment of unhealthy purposes. For example, such persons may crave attention, and some are quite proficient in disturbing an entire hospital ward or a church organization in order to achieve this end. A sympathetic clergyman, not equipped by training with an understanding of the problem, may unwittingly become the victim of their machinations. But not all patients will exploit their illness in this way. The clergyman must therefore learn to distinguish between the patient who ought to be given sympathy and the patient who will be harmed by sympathy. It is easy for the untrained clergyman to focus more than a healthy amount of attention on the secondary ends of illness or to make the mistake of trying to remove them before the fundamental problems are solved.

The techniques of the clergyman in the sickroom or in the privacy of his own office need to be examined in the light of modern knowledge of personality in health and illness. Frequently in the sickroom prayer and Scripture reading are utilized. In regard to such practices, the only general rule that can apply to all cases is not to do anything in the way of prayer or reading that the patient does not want to have done and that is not in harmony with the general character of the situation. Beyond this it is a matter of having sufficient understanding of the situation to know what to do and what not to do. Of these, the latter is frequently the more important, for it may be better to do nothing and thus let the case rest with the healing forces operative within the personality than to do the wrong thing. Thus one has known of prayers in a critical situation seriously damaging the courage and fighting spirit of a patient, and of prayers so inappropriately overemphasizing submission to the will of God that they confirmed the tendency toward chronic illness or even toward death. Even such minor matters as the clergyman's manner may be extremely significant. A clergyman may enter a sickroom with a gravity and solemnity that immediately suggest to the patient that the end is near. This can be disturbing to the patient. Or he may enter in a spirit of enthusiasm so inappropriate to the occasion that it irritates the patient. High-pressure techniques may fill the church on Sunday morning, but they have no place in a sickroom. On the other hand, an attitude of hopefulness, cheer, and understanding may be excellent medicine. Inner attitudes are better caught by contagion than by much verbalization and preaching, especially in a sickroom.

All these comments point to one basic fact, that the clergyman, along with other workers, faces the responsibility of so dealing with people as not to contribute to the development of their illness, either physical or mental, or to the intensification of anxiety, guilt, or hostility that is already a problem. A common theoretical objection to the idea that a clergyman should not create anxiety and guilt in persons is found in the belief that this is part of the job of the clergyman and is a necessity to the beginning of the Christian life. Clinically, it may be said that most of the people with whom clergymen deal already have much more anxiety and guilt than they can handle constructively. They do not need an intensification of these feelings; they need a kind of treatment which will lead to their release. On the other hand, it may also be stated that a person may be harmed by a too sudden or easy release from anxiety or guilt; that, properly understood and used, these may serve as real incentives to the reconstruction of personality. Receiving the forgiveness of God is not the free and easy experience that many theologians and preachers would have us believe. But in all of this it must be remembered that the ordination of any church does not place the clergyman in a position of infallibility.

That the clergyman may become a pathogenic agent is by no means the basic implication of the point of view developed in this book. More fundamental is the unique contribution which the clergyman, functioning through the usual techniques of his profession, may make toward the promotion of the health of the total person, and the responsibility that is his by virtue of his calling. The clergyman may become a pathogenic agent by virtue of his failure to carry out his more positive and constructive function. The crux of the problem lies in the understanding of the fundamental problems involved in health and illness, and the relation of religion and the work of the clergyman to these problems. A hopeful sign is the increasing number of clergymen who are becoming aware of their responsibility in matters of personal and community health and are seeking to enlarge their understanding and usefulness.

In this book we have stressed the central importance of integration and growth for the health of the personality. We have also indicated the function of religion in the development of personality, and the ways in which religion may function to produce illness or health. In the light of this, the role of the clergyman as being primarily in the field of prevention and secondarily in the area of cure should become clear. In a sense prevention and cure cannot be separated. They are two aspects of the same problem. But the tendency of religion to overemphasize what is frequently called the "cure of souls" requires that stress be laid on the more positive function of religion, that of prevention.

The relation of prevention and cure should be seen against the background of the concept of reversible and irreversible structure. The structuralization of function occurring throughout life, especially in the earlier years, indicates that this is the critical time and that more may be done here in the creation of a healthy outlook on life than can be done later in terms of change or cure. The intense interest of adolescents in religion, as well as the nature of the emotional problems of adolescents, should emphasize the important part religion may play at this time in the development of a personality structure that may become the foundation for a healthy maturity. The recognition of the fact that structure may become crystallized to the point where it is not reversible, and therefore where cure is not possible, should serve to clarify and emphasize the preventive aspects of religious work.

But prevention is a negative word. Merely to keep a person from becoming ill in the sense that illness is defined in this book is not possible. In these problems we are dealing with dynamic forces of life, which do not long remain stationary. The way to prevent illness is by the positive development of personality and the expansion of personality functions in the direction of their potentiality. The true function of religion is creative, and the role of the clergyman is that of helping persons achieve a way of life that produces values contributing to a well-integrated, wholesome, and growing personality.

The major function of religion in relation to illness is

that of prevention through the development of a way of life which reduces negative values to a minimum and increases positive values to a maximum. But this is an ideal formulation. Actually people will meet frustrations, conflicts, and crises which will strike at the foundations of their personality. At such times religious structure will go to pieces if it does not represent values deep enough and strong enough to meet the strain. The superficiality of much personal religion breeds disillusionment, bitterness, and cynicism in the face of deeper tragedies.

At the point where religious values and structure tend to break down under the pressure of immediate conflict and tension, the clergyman faces a major responsibility. It is here that the curative aspects of religion may serve a unique function, provided the realities of the situation are firmly grasped and provided the training of the clergyman has prepared him properly for his task. At such times the personality is in a somewhat fluid state out of which either a constructive solution may be achieved or an illness will be developed. At such times some individuals will be found lacking in sufficient inner resources to make even a small degree of stabilization and reconstruction possible, and illness will be both inevitable and not long in developing. In others, however, there will be sufficient inner resources provided adequate help can be given in discovering and utilizing them. In such persons the period of incubation of an illness may be rather long and this offers a real opportunity for constructive help. But, again, it is important for the clergyman to know what not to do as well as what to do. This involves the problem of pastoral techniques, which is too large to discuss here in detail. It is also important that the clergyman understand the ways in which religious symbols may be used for either illness or health. He should understand the importance of his relationship with his people as being of itself a source of strength and security. This involves not only his role as a clergyman, but even more the integrity of his own personality and the meanings and values vital in his own experience. A clergyman may strain so hard to do things for people in an attempt to help them that he misses entirely the deeper value of what he can be to people in a time of crisis or after an illness has developed.

The factual material presented in this book should indicate that the real contribution of the clergyman in matters of health is completely out of the realm of magic. It is also out of the realm of a rather crude type of mysticism which holds that if one prays to God everything will turn out all right. It is within the realm of laws governing personal and social life; not, indeed, man-made laws, but rather those written into the fundamental nature of our being. Neither religious formalities nor antireligious convictions provide impunity for the violation of these laws.

A radical re-evaluation of religion in terms of its actual as compared with its potential contribution is necessary today for the clergyman who would discharge his true function in the area of illness and health. During the past several decades religious leaders have placed considerable emphasis on the need for rethinking religion in order to effect an adjustment with some aspect of modern life. But much of this rethinking has turned out to be not much more than rationalization aimed at supporting religion. Along with this there has been a strong tendency for religious leaders to fall back on statements from men of science asserting the truth or value of religion. A danger of a book of this kind is that it will be used to confirm the smug complacency of certain religious persons who "have always known that religion had a great deal to do with illness and health." But the vitality and value of religion is to be found in only one place, in its functioning in human personality and culture. Here the problem is not one of rethinking or of defense of religion in general. It is a problem of discovering the actual functioning of religion in specific personalities and of evaluating this functioning in terms of the needs of the personality involved, and also in terms of the potentialities of both the personality and religion. Such a re-evaluation will cut through the tendency to accept religious phenomena at face value or to judge them from some particular theological or creedal point of view. Such re-evaluation of religion in a given personality would approach religion not as an isolated phenomenon, but in its relation to the total experience of the individual involved. It would require that the clergyman become truly expert in the psychology of religion and that he acquire a body of scientific knowledge in this area comparable to the scientific knowledge developed by the psychiatrist in regard to mental illness. It might be added that the best place to study the psychology of religion is not in a classroom or from a textbook, but in a laboratory such as a hospital or a parish. This should not interfere with any of the real functions of the clergyman. It is likely that the clergyman who feels it more important to understand his people than to help them will, in the end, render them a greater service.

The third implication of our material for the work of the clergymen has already been alluded to but deserves elaboration. It is the need for developing the techniques of religion on the basis of modern knowledge of personality in health and in illness and around the central function of religion in personality. By the techniques of religion are meant such practices as worship, preaching, religious education, pastoral work, and church administration.[4]

A full discussion of the problems involved in such development of the techniques of religion would require more than one volume. It is our purpose here to indicate a need rather than to supply a finished answer. As a matter of fact, no answer can be given today. The kind of development that is needed will require the co-operative work of many clergymen over a long period of time. It will require an experimental attitude based on the best available knowledge of man and his society, an objective attitude toward both the individual and cultural aspects of religion, and a clear conception of the role of the clergy in personality-culture relationships. In addition, it will require an appreciation of the symbolic and dynamic nature of religious expression, and an ability to evaluate critically the results of one's own work. It will also require the ability to distinguish between reality and symbol within both personality and the culture, as well as an understanding of the influences of cultural forces, religious and otherwise, on his own ideas, values, and goals. Beyond this, the clergyman must have a clear conception of meaning, values, and goals that are at once beyond man's reach, yet inherent in his nature and in a measure immediately attainable, and these must be formulated in such a manner as to make possible their application and actualization in the ever-present moment. Of course, all this might be said in religious language, but to do so would only blur the issue in many minds.

One of the problems faced by many serious-minded clergymen is that of what to do for persons who obviously need help and of how to do it. This problem is acute in many younger clergymen and theological students. Students particularly get the conviction that the training offered for other professions, such as psychiatry and social work, equips a man to render a greater service to persons than does the training given to theological students. Such convictions are amply reinforced by obvious facts, for theological education, on the whole, is centered in training the clergyman to maintain a tradition rather than to help persons in need. One result of this situation is the defection of many students from the ministry to the profession of psychiatry, psychology, or social work. In certain cases this is in no way to be regretted, though the basis for their decision is exceedingly unfortunate. Another result is the tendency of clergymen to take over the techniques of the psychiatrist in the belief that this is the way to make their ministry effective. Actually this does harm, because they are not adequately trained to use the methods of the psychiatrist and they do not function in the role of psychiatrist. Furthermore, in spite of certain similarities between the work of the psychiatrist and that of the clergyman, there are also vast differences which are not taken into account. The true answer to the problem is not to be found in taking over the techniques of another profession, which really leads to becoming something of a third- or fourth-rate psychiatrist or social worker, but rather the development of the techniques of religion. The clergyman has a unique contribution to make to the problems of personality and of culture, but this contribution may be made only through the development of the methods of the clergyman to the place where they are adequate for present-day needs. Of course, the problem is deeper than methods. The clergyman must have a living faith to express through his methods. This involves not only the "religion" of the clergyman but his total personality and his cultural relationships. In other words, the clergyman cannot hide behind symbols which mean little or nothing to his congregation and expect to make a significant contribution to modern life.

The development of the techniques of the clergyman is going forward at the present time, but not to the extent that it should be. One obstacle is the existing confusion in regard to the function of the clergyman. A related obstacle is a definition of the role of the clergyman in a way that makes him largely the promoter of an organization or the spokesman for traditional or institutional creeds and values, rather than a true servant of humanity. Many clergymen feel a deep conflict at this point. They see human needs for which they can do something, but their time and energy must be given to the promotion of programs or wrestling with church finances or similar activities. Many clergymen are conscious of the fact that their deeper functions in human life are being submerged by pressing demands of a more superficial nature. The effect of such frustrations on the personality of the clergyman is, in itself, a matter for serious concern. A sensitive clergyman may suffer within himself, while the situation may give others a splendid opportunity for the expression of strong ego drives. The definition of the role of the clergyman must be faced and solved by the church as a whole, but the individual clergyman may make a significant contribution to this larger process. Certainly there is need for a division of labor on the basis of the abilities of individual clergymen; but before the techniques of the clergyman may be fully developed, the problem of his true function must be clarified.

Another obstacle to the proper development of the techniques of religion is the character of most theological education. Students emerging from the average theological school today may be experts in Biblical criticism, in philosophical or theological argument, in certain literary devices for sermonizing, in textbook knowledge of psychology and sociology, and in other matters of more or less value. But they are not trained to deal with the fundamental material of the ministry—the human personality. Their thinking and work becomes book-centered, idea-centered, or program-centered, whereas it should be centered in personality. They may be in a position to evaluate the religious ideas of a person in the light of a given philosophical or theological position, but are not equipped to evaluate the function of that idea in the light of its influence on the health and illness of the person or in terms of the values represented in his life. This is related to the previous statement in regard to the need of the clergyman to be an expert in the kind of psychology of religion that grows out of a knowledge of personality.

Obviously, no extended discussion of theological education can be entered into at this point. However, there are few problems facing the church which in the long run are more critical than that of training its leadership. One much-needed revision is that of altering the viewpoint from which the curriculum is developed so that courses cease to be ends in themselves, but really become a means of equipping students to deal with some phase of the basic spiritual problem of modern life. Courses in theology, for example, may become vital and highly valuable when the content of theology is seen as the expression of the individual's endeavor to work out a Weltanschauung which may become the basis for the solution of inner conflict and the integration of the person with his universe. But taught as a series of cold, abstract ideas, in logical sequence, it becomes dull and spiritually deadening. The same holds for other disciplines found in the theological curriculum.

But some of the most fundamental lessons that the theological student must learn cannot be taught within the four walls of any classroom. They may be learned only as the student comes into firsthand relationship with human beings suffering from the maladies that afflict mankind. Such teaching can take place in the wards of mental or general hospitals, or in prisons, provided adequate theological and scientific supervision and instruction are present. The unique work of the Council for Clinical Training, Inc., in this field is worthy of recognition.[5] The fundamental principles developed by this organization for the training of theological students should be increasingly utilized in the expansion of this kind of education for clergymen. Such training is absolutely essential for the student who hopes to discharge, to even a moderate degree, the responsibility which today is falling on the clergyman for the health and well-being of the community.

Another problem in theological education has highly significant implications for the health of the church and the community. It is the problem of selection of candidates for the ministry, and the application of personality and mental health considerations in this selection. At the present time requirements for admission to most first-rate theological schools are largely academic. Without relaxing academic standards in any way, much more provision should be made for considering the mental health and personality qualifications of candidates for the ministry. Some schools are doing this in a limited way, but not to the extent that it should be done.[6] Such selection involves the problem of the relation of personality needs to the choice of a vocation, particularly in the religious field. It involves also the problem of the religious interpretation of vocational choices. The

choice of a vocation may be subject to a religious interpretation and motivation that expresses and conceals unhealthy
tendencies; or, religious interpretations and motivations may
operate in the direction of a healthy choice. Along with im-
proved methods of selection aiming at the elimination of
certain candidates, more facilities should be provided for
helping theological students to work out their emotional
problems before entering the ministry. This does not imply
that theological students are more in need of this than are
students entering other professions, for such is not the case.
However, the work of the clergyman is such that proper personality qualifications and sound mental health are especially important. The present neglect of the mental health
of theological students is a major weakness in theological
education, which may lead to serious consequences in the
community.

THE RELATIONSHIP BETWEEN CLERGYMEN AND PHYSICIANS

In addition to these implications for the work of the clergyman, the material presented in this book carries a clear indication of the need for a co-operative relationship between
the physician and the clergyman. Not since the rise of scientific medicine has a point of view been developed which
offers such a sound basis for physician-clergyman relationships. The organism-environment concept in medicine both
broadens and deepens the concept of illness and health so
that the place and function of various professional workers
become clarified and the interrelationship of these workers
is seen in a more helpful perspective. If the thesis of this
book is sound, physicians and clergymen must learn to co-
operate, each serving his distinctive function, in grappling
with the problems of illness and health.

The practical basis for physician-clergy co-operation is the
welfare of the patient. This means that clergymen and physicians alike must lay aside personal prejudices as unwarranted
and as beneath the true dignity of their professions. In this

it is likely that the clergymen will have the easier task, as there seems to be more prejudice in the minds of physicians against religion than in the minds of clergymen against medicine. In matters medical, the physician is usually considered to be the only one qualified to render an opinion. But in matters religious, everyone considers himself more or less an authority and regards his personal views as final. Unfortunate experiences in or with religion have left many persons, including physicians, prejudiced at the outset of any discussion of physician-clergy relationships. The highly exaggerated and unscientific claims of religious healing groups also has an adverse influence. However, the more physicians come to understand the great variety and nature of the factors that influence and create illness and health, and the more expert they become in understanding their patient in these terms, the more they will appreciate the contribution of the clergyman to the recovery of the patient. Of course, this will also involve marked advances in the understanding and techniques of the clergyman in this area of service. In spite of all the theoretical arguments, it still remains true that no religious ministry may be highly preferable to a ministry not based on sound understanding and adequate procedures. But in the welfare of the patient these professions have a common meeting ground and a joint responsibility, even though this may not be recognized in all cases.

The fundamental problems in physician-clergy relationships are in the area of understanding rather than in the area of practical procedures. Given the proper attitude and understanding on the part of each group, practical procedures may be easily developed. On the practical level there is need for experimentation and research, and the proper place for this is the hospital and sickroom. Clinical material, accurately recorded and honestly evaluated, should become the basis for studies in this field. But behind all of this a cooperative attitude on the part of each profession is essential.

Professors in theological schools have been known to criticize the idea that the physician can teach the young clergyman a great deal about sick persons. The idea of clinical training for clergymen is sometimes frowned upon for the same reason. But the fact remains that the physician has gained considerable knowledge about sick people that is of great help to the clergyman in discharging his proper function. A comparable body of knowledge in regard to the effect of religious ministrations on the ill has not been acquired by clergymen, but is being developed slowly. This is a task on which progress will be made during the next decade or two. But in the meantime it is highly probable that medical students could profit from a properly presented course in the psychology of religion and the function and aims of the clergyman in the sickroom. Certainly there is an urgent need for the sharing of knowledge and skills and the development of a higher degree of mutual understanding between clergymen and physicians.

The Relationship Between Clergymen and Social Workers

The implications of our basic thesis do not stop with physician-clergy relationships. They go on to the relationships between the clergyman and the social worker. The social worker, whether in case work or group work, is dealing with organism-environment relationships, and is particularly trying to help individuals work out solutions to problems related to social adjustment and to develop constructive attitudes which may lead to a more healthy way of life. While the social worker deals primarily with the manifestations of illness on the social level, her work is of great significance for the total personality and for the group. Unless she be a mere technician, handing out food or money, she cannot escape dealing with the fundamental interpretations of meaning and value in the life of the client. Here her work has highly significant religious implications. The clergyman, on the other hand, cannot discharge his responsibilities without converging on the field of social work. At some points the goals of the clergyman and the social worker are similar, but their approaches and techniques differ. Certainly effective work on the part of the clergyman should lead persons to better social adjustments. An understanding of organism-environment relationships as they affect social adjustments and religion require a close understanding and co-operation between the professional workers in these areas. Such understanding will dispel the feeling that the social worker is encroaching on the province of the clergyman and, on the other hand, that the clergyman has nothing to offer the social worker. It should also help to dispel the illusion that any professional worker in medicine, religion, or social work can definitely delimit the area of his interest and work, and post "no trespassing" signs, without at the same time limiting his usefulness and hurting the persons with whom he is working. Certainly there is a place in many churches for a well-trained social worker, and a properly trained clergyman can make a real contribution on the staff of social agencies. A basic practical step is the sharing of understanding and skills between representatives of these two professions. An excellent place to begin this is in the schools where these workers are trained. Courses in the philosophy and practice of social work have a real place in the theological curriculum, and courses in the psychology of religion and the function of the church and the clergyman in society are pertinent to social work training.

CONCLUSION

In conclusion, and contrary to the opinions of some people, let it be said that religion is not dead, neither is it something that has served its purpose at more infantile levels of racial development and should therefore cease to be. So long as man faces tragedies and suffering, so long as man searches for the meaning and value of life, so long as he finds some answer to these questions that lifts him above the level of animal existence, there will be religion. So long as human nature is so constituted that one way of life leads to illness individually or socially, while another leads to health and a measure of personal fulfillment, there will be religion. So long as human nature is so constituted biologically, psychologically, and spiritually that personal life cannot exist without group life, and so long as personal and group life are bound so inextricably together, there will be religion. So long as the question of right and wrong, of purposes, goals, and ideals, holds the significance that is true at present, there will be religion. So long as man is required to learn how to handle his fears, hates, guilts, and loves so that they become life-building rather than life-destroying, there will be religion. So long as man, the finite, reaches out for the Infinite source of life and of light, there will be religion. To the mature Christian, so long as the ideal portrayed by the life of Christ presents itself as ultimately attainable but yet unattained, there will be religion. The symbols and forms of religion should and must change, and in so far as religion is burdened by illusions these must give way to a more mature grasp of reality. But religion, in the sense of the inner spirit and faith of man in the potential resources of the universe, is essential to the life, growth, and fulfillment of personality. Rather than being faced with extinction, religion today is being faced with as urgent an opportunity as has ever been present in the long history of mankind.

REFERENCES

1. Wolfe, T. P., "Psychotherapy in the general hospital," *American Journal of Psychiatry*, 95: 1939, p. 1307.
2. Dunbar, H. Flanders, *Emotions and Bodily Changes*, introduction to 2nd ed., p. xvii. New York, 1938.
   See also *Psychosomatic Medicine, A Quarterly Journal.*
3. *Mental Health*, p. 205. Lancaster, Pa., 1939.
4. For a study of one aspect of this problem see "The clergy and community education for mental hygiene," by Carroll A. Wise, in *Mental Hygiene*, 25: 1941, pp. 30-42.

5. For further information on the Council for Clinical Training, Inc., write to the Council office, New York.
6. For more detailed information on this point see "The role of the clergy in relation to the mentally ill," by Carroll A. Wise, in *Mental Health*, p. 438. Lancaster, Pa., 1939.

INDEX

Abnormality, different from normality in degree, 27

Absolute, 143

Accidents, emotional factor in, 26

Adjustment, of organism and culture, 252

Adolescent, and idealization, 240; and identification, 240

Age level of conflict, guide to type of reaction, 56

Aged, assets of, 50; disorders of, 39, 48; physical disabilities of, 48; personality disorders of, 48; problems of, 51; and religion, 51

Alcoholism, 37-39, 49; causes of, 37; personality changes from, 37; and transference, 224-226

Alexander, Franz, quoted, 16, 163, 244

Allergy, and asthma and hay fever, 16-17

Amblystoma, 67

Amnesia, 55

Analogy, 142

Angina pectoris, emotional factor in, 22; and personality, 94

Anthropologists, and approach to organism-environment relationships, 79

Anthropomorphism, 144

Anxiety, 72, 73; as contributing factor to illness, 19, 25, 26

Anxiety hysteria, 54

Anxiety neurosis, 54

Arteries, hardening of, 35

Asthma, and allergy, 16-17; and emotion, 16-17, 20

Atonement, 222

Autonomy, 197, 250

Balance, danger of lack of, 199; in religious symbolism, 199-201

Beethoven, 228

Beliefs, dynamic sources of, 130; main premise of, 130; and environment, 128

Bible, 5, 124, 139, 181, 203, 216, 239

Binger, Dr. Carl, quoted, 20

Biologist, insight of, 120

Blanton, Dr. Smiley, quoted, 225-226

Blindness, 55

Blood pressure, high, and emotion, 16, 29

Bock, Dr. Arlie V., quoted, 17

Boisen, Dr. A. T., 217, 234, 245

Bowers, Anna M., quoted, 244

Brain injury, 35

"Bread of life," as symbol, 140

Bronchitis, chronic, emotional factor in, 22-23

Bronner, Augusta F., quoted, 244

Brooks, Dr. Harlow, quoted, 15

Bunyan, John, 103

Calvinism, 198

Campbell, C. M., quoted, 77, 129

Cannon, Walter B., quoted, 22, 71, 72, 76

Carcinoma, 92; incidence in paranoid, cycloid, schizoid and epileptoid groups, 92

Cardiac debility, emotional factor in, 23

Cardiovascular diseases, emotional factor in, 21-22

"Carnal," 240

Case History, of Mary Jones, 42, 103, 126, 132, 151-152, 157, 175, 185, 193, 203, 213-214, 240; of Mrs. Smith, 4-5, 8, 9-10, 33

Catatonia, 40

Catholics, 157

Cerebral arteriosclerosis, 49

Character disorders, 39, 59

Charlatans, 8, 10

Child, C. M., 65